LET THERE BE LIGHT

Darius Dinshah

*   *   *

Based on the work of
Col. Dinshah P. Ghadiali

FOURTH EDITION

*   *   *   *   *

DINSHAH HEALTH SOCIETY
P O Box 707
Malaga NJ 08328 USA

Dinshah P. Ghadiali
(1873-1966)

CONTENTS

First edition, May 1985. Second edition, April 1995
Third edition, June 1996. Fourth edition, December 1997
Copyright© 1997, 1996, 1995, 1985, Dinshah Health Society, Malaga NJ 08328.
ISBN 0-933917-17-1
(German edition, 1989, "Es werde Licht." ISBN 0-933917-03-1.)

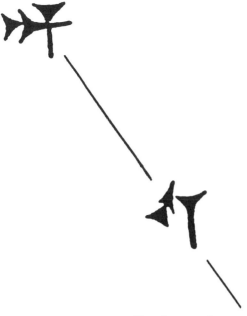

To those who seek an enlightened path

in the art of healing

<u>LET THERE BE LIGHT</u>

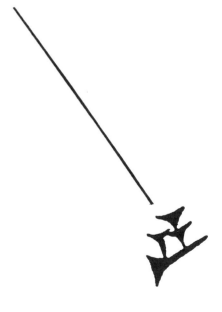

FOREWORD

1. Dinshah P. Ghadiali, born in India, was my father. His last name often seemed too difficult for American tongues, so he preferred to be called by his first name. He was quite proud of having earned the rank of Colonel in the New York City Police Air Reserve. In time, he became widely known as "Col. Dinshah." I was named Darius Dinshah Ghadiali, in keeping with an Indian custom of children using their father's first name as their middle name. However, to the American mind, "Col. Dinshah" implied that Dinshah was his and my last name; so to simplify matters I legally dropped the "Ghadiali" as did my mother and most of my siblings. Now, when you read "Dinshah" in this book it is as he wished; and it means THE Dinshah, my father.

2. Dinshah was born to a family of Zoroastrian faith (sometimes called "The Religion of Light"). He zealously practiced his beliefs, with sincere respect for all persuasions. One of his favorite quotations was from the Bible, "And God said, 'Let there be Light...'" which now stands out as the fitting title for this book on the Dinshah method of healing with Light.

3. Much of this book was published in 1978 as "The Spectro-Chrome System," but with the wealth of important added information (1985), it appeared appropriate to use a new title rather than another edition of the "System." It was revised, with additional chapters in 1995, and reprinted with few changes in later editions.

* * * * *

4. Few significant inventions are created by one person from conception to fruition, and this holds true for Spectro-Chrome as it is based on the perceptive efforts of several forebears. Dinshah gave unstinting credit to them for the threads of knowledge they spun and which he wove into the completed fabric of Spectro-Chrome. Some of his preceptors were Sir Isaac Newton, Dr. William Wollaston, Joseph von Fraunhofer, Gustav Kirshhoff, Robert von Bunsen, Sir William Crookes, Dr. Seth Pancoast, and Dr. Edwin D. Babbitt. It is beyond the scope of this book for a discourse on the contribution each made toward the evolution of Spectro-Chrome; for a comprehensive study on the subject, refer to the "Spectro-Chrome Metry Encyclopedia," and video "My Spectro-Chrome."

* * * * *

5. It has been said that if you build a better mousetrap the world will beat a path to your door. This has been so for some but for others the path has been fraught with obstacles when they attempted to promote their unconventional ideas or products. Whether the proposed improvement is in science, medicine, engineering or other structured field, the resistance to change is often formidable. Such opposition may stem from ignorance, avarice, jealousy, or similar human failing. It can be said that, for whatever reasons, Dinshah fought for almost every inch of ground he gained.

6. At this time (1997), U.S. Food and Drug Administration regulations prevent us from selling Spectro-Chrome Color projectors (or their parts) as they have been held to be medical devices. If you cannot buy the necessary equipment, how will you proceed? Fortunately, the problem is not so complex as might be imagined, and is solved in Chapters three and fourteen, Color Production and Inexpensive Projector Plans respectively. Then, as an open-minded health seeker, you will have at hand one of the safest, most useful therapies ever designed.

7. While many professionals used Spectro-Chrome in the past and a few presently do, this is basically a laypersons' therapy. At first glance, some feel Spectro-Chrome is "quite complicated", but this is the basic procedure: Select a Color, check for a recommended tonation time (Forecast), remove clothing from the area to be treated, turn on the projector and relax. And, Color selection at its simplest: Lemon when there is no fever, Blue if there is, an occasional Magenta on the chest, and a Color from Chapter six if a particular organ is involved. Obviously, much more can be accomplished when all the information in this book is employed though not all details are necessarily important in every case. There are only 32 pages of basic instructions (Chapters two through six); read them and then re-read them. It is your prerogative to test Spectro-Chrome, make it part of your day-to-day life, or reject it.   Read on, and see the Light.

DINSHAH HEALTH SOCIETY

Darius Dinshah, Pres.

* * * * *

IN APPRECIATION

When Dinshah died in 1966, there was concern in many quarters as to how the work of Spectro-Chrome would continue.

It has been said that when there is a need there is always someone to carry on. Unfortunately, what was needed was not just an understudy but a person capable of creative work in his own right.

The earliest task for this person was to continue the advance of Spectro-Chrome, maintaining its original integrity while cracking artificial barriers to free dissemination of the science. Then, the necessity of matching the knowledge of the past with materials currently available. Finally, the high desirability of easier access to concepts sometimes not easily discerned.

In reading countless comments of those who have learned that the work of Spectro-Chrome is continuing and/or studied earlier editions of this work, it is evident that the right someone appeared – brother Darius.

With love and respect

Roshan Dinshah

Jal J. Dinshah

* * * * *

NOTE: The information in this volume is for personal enlightenment. Though it is presented in good faith, neither the author nor the publisher can assume responsibility or liability for any results, direct or consequential, from experimental or practical application of this information. Whether the advice of a professional health practitioner is sought and/or followed also is the responsibility of the user or reader.

PREFACE

1. Dinshah was of course the most vocal supporter of Spectro-Chrome therapy. Of all the professional therapists he trained, Dr. Kate W. Baldwin was the most notable, and she ran a close second to him in enthusiasm.

2. Dr. Baldwin held the position of Senior Surgeon for 23 years at Philadelphia Woman's Hospital. For the last three years of her tenure there, she used Spectro-Chrome methods in the hospital, as well as in her private medical practice. That she was thoroughly versed in the principles and effects of Spectro-Chrome may be inferred from the following abstract of a paper she presented at a clinical meeting of the section on Eye, Ear, Nose and Throat Diseases of the Medical Society of the State of Pennsylvania, held at the Medico-Chirurgical Hospital in Philadelphia, on October 12, 1926. The original paper is not available so the abstract as it was printed in the Atlantic Medical Journal of April 1927 will speak for her:

THE THERAPEUTIC VALUE OF LIGHT AND COLOR

Kate W. Baldwin, M.D., F.A.C.S

Former Senior Surgeon, Woman's Hospital, Philadelphia, Pa.

In the effort to obtain relief from suffering, many of the more simple but potent measures have been overlooked while we have grasped at the obscure and complicated.

Sunlight is the basic source of all life and energy upon earth. Deprive plant or animal life of light, and it soon shows the lack and ceases to develop. Place a seed in the very best of soil or a human being in a palace, shut out the light, and what happens? Without food (in the usual sense of the term) man can live many days; without liquids a much shorter time; but not at all without the atmosphere which surrounds him at all times and to which he pays so little attention. The forces on which life mostly depends are placed nearly or quite beyond personal control.

For centuries scientists have devoted untiring effort to discover means for the relief or cure of human ills and restoration of the normal functions. Yet in neglected light and color there is a potency far beyond that of drugs and serums.

In order that the whole body may function perfectly, each organ must be a hundred percent perfect. When the spleen, the liver, or any other organ falls below normal, it simply means that the body laboratories have not provided the required materials with which to work, either because they are not functioning as a result of some disorder of the internal mechanism, or because they have not been provided with the necessary materials. Before the body can appropriate the required elements, they must be separated from the waste matter. Each element gives off a characteristic color wave. The prevailing color wave of hydrogen is red, and that of oxygen is blue, and each element in turn gives off its own special color wave. Sunlight, as it is received by the body, is split into the prismatic colors and their combinations as white light is split by passage through a prism. Everything on the red side of the spectrum is more or less stimulating, while the blue is sedative. There are many shades of each color, and each is produced by a little different wave length. Just as sound waves are tuned to each other and produce harmony or discords, so color waves may be tuned, and only so can they be depended on always to produce the same results.

If one requires a dose of castor oil, he does not go to a drug-store and request a little portion from each bottle on the shelves. I see no virtue, then, in the use of the whole white light as a therapeutic measure when the different colors can give what is required without taxing the body to rid itself of that for which it has no use, and which may do more or less harm. If the body is sick it should be restored with the least possible effort. There is no more accurate or easier way than by giving the color representing the lacking elements, and the body will, through its radioactive forces [the aura], appropriate them and so restore the normal balance. Color is the simplest and most accurate therapeutic measure yet developed.

For about six years I have given close attention to the action of colors in restoring the body functions, and I am perfectly honest in saying that, after nearly thirty-seven years of active hospital and private practice in medicine and surgery, I can produce quicker and more accurate results with colors than with any or all other methods combined—and with less strain on the patient. In many cases, the functions have been restored after the classical remedies have failed. Of course, surgery is necessary in some cases, but the results will be quicker and better if color is used before and after operation. Sprains, bruises and traumata of all sorts respond to color as to no other treatment. Septic conditions yield, regardless of the specific organism. Cardiac lesions, asthma, hay fever, pneumonia, inflammatory conditions of the eyes, corneal ulcers, glaucoma, and cataracts are relieved by the treatment.

The treatment of carbuncles with color is easy compared to the classical methods. One woman with a carbuncle involving the back of the neck from mastoid to mastoid, and from occipital ridge to the first dorsal vertebra, came under color therapy after ten days of the very best of attention. From the first day of color application, no opiates, not even sedatives, were required. This patient was saved much suffering, and she has little scar.

The use of color in the treatment of burns is well worth investigating by every member of the profession. In such cases the burning sensation caused by the destructive forces may be counteracted in from twenty to thirty minutes, and it does not return. True burns are caused by the destructive action of the red side of the spectrum, hydrogen predominating. Apply oxygen by the use of the blue side of the spectrum, and much will be done to relieve the nervous strain, the healing processes are rapid, and the resulting tissues soft and flexible.

In very extensive burns in a child of eight years of age there was almost complete suppression of urine for more than 48 hours, with a temperature of 105 to 106 degrees. Fluids were forced to no effect, and a more hopeless case is seldom seen. Scarlet was applied just over the kidneys at a distance of eighteen inches for twenty minutes, all other areas being covered. Two hours after, the child voided eight ounces of urine.

In some unusual and extreme cases that had not responded to other treatment, normal functioning has been restored by color therapy. At present, therefore, I do not feel justified in refusing any case without a trial. Even in cases where death is inevitable, much comfort may be secured.

There is no question that light and color are important therapeutic media, and that their adoption will be of advantage to both the profession and the people.

* * * * *

3. Dr. Baldwin's sentiments are concisely stated in one sentence, in a letter from her to another doctor, "I would close my office tonight never to reopen, if I could not use Spectro-Chrome." What a magnificent champion of Spectro-Chrome! If only we could find another like her now.

* * * * *

4. In this age of expanding technology, the methods for restoring and maintaining health are growing also. The expanding list may include allopathic and homeopathic medicine, osteopathy, chiropractic, naturopathy, reflexology, acupuncture, acupressure, radionics, kinesiology, magneto-therapy, iridology, hypnotism, music, herbology, and sound. Under differing circumstances, one or more of these could be helpful to a patient. With so many modalities from which to choose, why then do we publish this book? Simply, that after a lifetime of witnessing the value of the Spectro-Chrome system, we believe that the world has not only the right but the need to have this system added to the above series. It has been eminently successful for well over 75 years. This book, with the most thorough compilation ever available on the practical application of Color, will hasten the day when Spectro-Chrome will take its rightful place as an important means of restoring and maintaining health.

5. As knowledge in the therapeutic field grows in so many diverse directions, sooner or later conscientious healers will be impelled to take an eclectic view of their calling. Color therapy (and Spectro-Chrome in particular) must be among the choices available to them. Until that time comes, this book can help you to help yourself by using Spectro-Chrome with or instead of other methods. It must be emphasized that while the list of diseases and conditions given in this book is comprehensive in order to be as useful as possible, we do not expect all conditions to be treatable without professional care. Among the many situations which are likely to be beyond the scope of self-help are severe dehydration, heart failure, conditions requiring oxygen therapy, and certain first-aid measures. But even in such crises, why not use Spectro-Chrome also? It just might make the difference between life and death.

6. In order to properly treat a disease by its medical name, it is considered necessary to have an accurate diagnosis of the condition, with of course the possibility of error. To a large extent, the Spectro-Chrome system can avoid the pitfall of mis-diagnosis because its safety and simplicity can lead to its use without differential diagnosis; this is covered in detail in Chapters five and six.

7. At this point, suffice it to say that if your practitioner is not eclectic (as Dr. Baldwin surely was), then it is in your best interests to be. After all, whose health or life is at stake?

* * * * *

CHAPTER ONE

DINSHAH P. GHADIALI
and
SPECTRO-CHROME

1873   Born in Bombay, India, on November 28th.

1876   Entered Bhulia Mehta's primary school.

1881   Began high school.

1884   Became Assistant to the Professor of mathematics and science at Wilson College. Was awarded prizes for proficiency in English, Persian, and religion. He eventually learned eight oriental and eight occidental languages, some of them fluently.

1886   Took Bombay University examination.

1887   Gave experimental demonstrations in chemistry and physics at seven institutions of learning. Began study of medicine. Conducted his own business of installing electric lights, doorbells, burglar alarms, annunciator systems, etc.

1891   Began his oratorical career, on spiritual and scientific subjects with "The Electric Light: Its Production, Practicability, and Cheapness." Was initiated as a Fellow in the Theosophical Society; there, he commenced earnest study of "occultism" (true meaning: hidden knowledge; modern usage for devil worship, etc. is incorrect). Became a lacto-vegetarian and teetotaler; this regimen he practiced and ardently advocated for the rest of his life.

1892   Erected several electric light installations. Was appointed Superintendent of Telephone and Telegraph for Dholpur State.

1893   Signed on as an Electrical Engineer (seaman) with the Peninsular and Oriental Steamship Company; went to London, England, and returned to India.

1894   Was appointed Electrical Engineer of Patiala State, and Mechanical Engineer of the Umballa Flour Mills.

1896   Made his first visit to the United States. Met Thomas Edison, Nikola Tesla and other noted scientists. Lectured on x-rays and radioactivity; the New York Times and other newspapers termed him the "Parsee Edison." Returned to India to continue his professions there.

1897   Campaigned for a number of civil reforms throughout India; and developed his medical practice. During the bubonic plague of this and following years, the accepted medical treatment saved only 40% of the unfortunate sufferers. Over 60% of Dinshah's patients recovered by his closely watching the strength of the heart, using caffeine, ammonia, and other stimulants when needed; and the utilization of iodine-terchloride, a non-official preparation. His later studies relating elements to Colors would classify this as having Color emanations of Lemon and Green.

The year 1897 also marked a turning point in his medical thinking: The niece of one of his Theosophical Society friends was dying from mucous colitis. The learned physician who was ministering to her used the then accepted drugs to no avail. Dinshah was aware of the theory of chromopathy, having read "The Principles of Light and Color" (1876), by Dr. Edwin D. Babbitt; and "Blue and Red Light, or Light and its Rays as Medicine" (1877), by Dr. Seth Pancoast.

Convinced that the only hope for her recovery lay in an unorthodox healing method, he proceeded according to Dr. Babbitt's technique. The light from a kerosene lantern, with an Indigo-colored glass bottle used as a filter, was shone on her. Milk was placed in another bottle of the same color as the filter bottle and then exposed to Sunlight; she later drank the milk. The urgent straining to evacuate, which occurred perhaps a hundred times a day, abated to ten after one day of treatment; after three days she was able to get out of bed. This case was the beginning, but twenty-three years passed before his researches culminated in the healing system he called **SPECTRO-CHROME.**

1899 Became stage manager of the Bombay Theater and installed there one of the earliest electric motion-picture projectors. He also appeared on-stage as an actor.

1900 Established the "Electro-Medical Hall" at Ajmer, India, for healing by color, magneto-therapy, electro-therapy, suggesto-therapy, as well as orthodox medicine.

1901 Opened another Electro-Medical Hall, in Surat, India. Dinshah became known for his successful treatment of bubonic plague, and so-called incurable diseases.

1902 Married Manek H. Mehta.

1904 Was elected Chairman of the "Nanpura Parsee Community", a group organized to help the poor.

1905 Started his own weekly newspaper, "Impartial"; his editorials exposing corrupt officials created an uproar.

Stricken with tuberculosis, Dinshah was given six months to live by a medical consultant who advised him, "Take plenty of rest, eat some meat and drink some wine for strength". Dinshah steadfastly maintained his principles, and recovered his health by following a rigorous regimen of work and physical training with no meat, no wine, and LESS rest.

1908 Left India and travelled around Europe promoting some of his inventions.

1909 Lectured on Prohibition in London, England. In order to provide drinkers with a substitute, he began selling fruit juices (processed in Switzerland) under the name "Alcohol-Free Wines".

1911 Emigrated to the United States with his wife and two children.

1912 Despite his qualifications, steady employment was not his lot; privations eventually caused Manek to leave the family and return to India. Developed the "Dinshah Automobile Engine Fault-Finder" and an "Anti-Forgery Electric Pen"; and formed companies to market them.

1913 Began manufacture of the "Fault-Finder." He was offered $100,000 for the invention, but later donated it to the United States government for use on aircraft engines.

1914 Organized the "Dinshah Photokinephone Corporation" for developing a sound-on-film, shutterless, flickerless motion-picture projector. A patent application was later filed on the apparatus.

1917 Was naturalized as a citizen of the United States.

1918 Received a commission as a Captain in the New York City Police Reserve. Joined the American Association of Progressive Medicine.

1919 Was appointed Governor of the New York City Police Aviation School, and later was commissioned Colonel and Commander of the New York Police Reserve Air Service. Two aircraft were obtained from the federal government for patrolling the New York harbor. He flew the first police airmail, New York to Philadelphia. For his meritorious service to the city, New York Mayor John Hyland awarded Dinshah the Liberty Medal.

       Served as Vice-President of the Allied Medical Associations of America, and the National Association of Drugless Practitioners. Healing was always in his mind, even if not at the forefront.

1920 While the year 1897 marked a turning point in Dinshah's thinking, 1920 was pivotal in many other ways. His research completed, in April he delivered the first lecture on Spectro-Chrome therapy. The Spectro-Chrome Institute was established in New York City. The first class for training in the use of Spectro-Chrome began in December with 27 present.

       In the next four years he conducted 26 such classes in cities from coast-to-coast, with 800 in attendance. Their occupations covered most branches of the medical profession, as well as many laypersons. He eventually taught one hundred classes.

       This then was the pattern for the second 46 years of his life: Lecture, write books on Spectro-Chrome, teach classes, design Color equipment and accessories such as the Sympathometer, Itisometer, Spirometer, Antinude, and Nurmand (descriptions are in Chapter Four); and defend himself and his work in numerous litigations. Lawsuits were fought in Portland Oregon, Cleveland Ohio, Buffalo New York, Wilmington Delaware, Washington D.C., Brooklyn New York, and twice in Camden New Jersey. His defense was successful in Buffalo (1931) against a charge of grand larceny, – that the complainant was defrauded because Spectro-Chrome could not have any effect on diseases; Dinshah proved that it did with several lay and medical practitioners testifying for him (see Chapter 11, A Triumph for Spectro-Chrome). In Camden he won by documenting that he was of the white race and therefore should not be deported, 17 years after he had been naturalized.

       The rest of the litigations were lost, resulting in fines ranging from $25 to $20,000; and prison sentences from two months to five years, of which 18 months were served. These continuing setbacks he bore stoically with an unbounded confidence in the value of his System and its eventual vindication and acceptance.

1922   Divorce from Manek granted on grounds of desertion.

1923   Married Irene Grace Hoger. The union was blessed with eight children, the last born in 1947.

1924   Acquired a 23-acre property in Malaga New Jersey, which then became the Spectro-Chrome Institute headquarters.

1933   Wrote the **Spectro-Chrome Metry Encyclopedia** which has come to be known as an authoritative treatise on Color therapy. As a definitive work, other authors often quote material in it.

1937   Ran as an independent candidate for Governor of New Jersey. Came in next to last in the vote count.

1939   Made an around-the-world tour: lecturing and opening two offices in India for promoting Spectro-Chrome.

1941   Dissolved the corporate entity of Spectro-Chrome Institute; chartered the Dinshah Spectro-Chrome Institute, a non-profit corporation. Institute activities severely hampered by a U.S. Post Office fraud-order. This is an administrative procedure, not a lawsuit, ordering the local postmaster to return to the senders all mail addressed to the "offender", stamped with the notation, "FRAUDULENT, Mail to this address returned by order of Post-master General". The order stands to this day.

1944   Donated a new fire-engine and siren to the Malaga Volunteer Fire Company. His appreciation of the community's need for more modern fire protection turned out to be quite prophetic.

1945   A calamitous fire on January 2nd totally destroyed the Institute's main building, despite the efforts of several fire battalions. Dinshah lost all his scientific demonstration equipment, invention models, library, case histories, personal belongings, etc. The loss materially handicapped his defense in the Brooklyn lawsuit which was fought three months later, and in the Camden litigation of 1947. The disaster also rendered some of his books out-of-print, but many others were separately warehoused.

1947   A six-week trial in Camden, N.J., initiated by the Federal Food and Drug Administration, resulted in a fine of $20,000 and probation for Dinshah for five years with the stipulation that he dissolve the Institute and dissociate himself from any form of promotion of Spectro-Chrome. He also was ordered to surrender for destruction all books in his possession relating to Spectro-Chrome; their value may have amounted to $250,000. He was permitted to keep one set of his writings for his personal library.

1953   His probation completed, Dinshah organized another non-profit corporation, the Visible Spectrum Research Institute. The Color devices, now called "Visible Spectrum Projectors", were sold with a warning stating that according to then-accepted medical views the Projectors had no curative or therapeutic value.

1958   The U.S. Food and Drug Administration obtained a permanent injunction against the Visible Spectrum Research Institute, preventing shipment across State lines of Color Projectors and books pertaining to them. Even some books unrelated to Spectro-Chrome were banned (Freedom of the Press?). The Court held that even though there were warnings on the

Projectors and books, stating their lack of orthodox medical acceptance, they were the same misbranded articles of the 1947 decision against the previous corporation (res adjudicata). The injunction still stands.

1958 The injunction compelled Dinshah to limit most of his activities to the State of New Jersey where he sold a few Projectors and books, and delivered a few lectures. It was a time of forced semi-retirement.

1966 April 30th. Dinshah ceased his work on this level. The body was cremated, in accordance with his wishes.

   The name Dinshah means "King of Duty" and a man could not have been named more aptly. He was a man with faults and foibles, as any man may have; but when duty called the bell had to ring only once.

Shanti

1966 Having been raised in the service of the Institutes, three of Dinshah's sons assumed the responsibilities of conducting the Institute's affairs: Darius, Trustee and President; Roshan, Trustee, Vice-President and Treasurer; Jal, Secretary (and later, Trustee). A new compact Color projector was designed and marketed in New Jersey. Darius spoke each year at several meetings. Some material which could not be sent across State boundaries was written and printed in many States.

1975 The Institute's Trustees, and members at their 1975 annual Convention meetings, decided that it was too great a handicap to continue working under the Court injunction. The corporate entity of the Visible Spectrum Research Institute was therefore dissolved.

   November 15th. The Dinshah Health Society was registered as a non-profit corporation, with the express aim of stimulating interest in, and promulgating knowledge of, lesser known methods of restoring and maintaining health.

1977 The U.S. Internal Revenue Service approved the Society's application for status as a non-profit, scientific, educational organization, for tax exemption purposes.

1978 **The Spectro-Chrome System** was written when the Society became aware of the need for a concise manual on the Dinshah method of Color therapy.

1985 Requests for more in-depth instructions on Spectro-Chrome resulted in the rewriting and expansion of "The Spectro-Chrome System". Due to the considerable amount of new material, it was retitled **Let There Be Light**.

1989 Increasing interest overseas prompted the Society to translate and print "Let There Be Light" in the German language: **Es werde Licht**. Later, other Society literature also was printed in German.

1993 **My Spectro-Chrome**, a six-hour video monolog, was produced by the Society to increase the means of promoting and understanding Spectro-Chrome therapy.

1995 Second edition of **Let There Be Light**, containing much new material, is published.

✳ ✳ ✳ ✳ ✳

CHAPTER TWO

SPECTRO-CHROME DEFINITIONS

This book is a discourse on Spectro-Chrome technique but only a compendium on its theories. While some reasoning is given here, it is not practical to explain everything in detail. For a complete understanding of its genesis and principles, refer to the "Spectro-Chrome Metry Encyclopedia", and video presentation, "My Spectro-Chrome".

* * * * *

1. TONATION. Shining a Spectro-Chrome Color on the body, or a part of the body, is called a TONATION; you TONATE with a Color. A tonation is normally <u>one Color</u> on a given area (or areas) <u>for one hour</u>, at a Forecast time when possible. When you are instructed to tonate both front and back areas, e.g., #4-5-18, it means this: tonate areas #4 and 5 (front areas) at one tonation and area #18 (a back area) at another tonation (if two projectors are available for simultaneous use, see instructions in Chapter four, section H). When instructed to tonate two or more Colors, one Color is tonated for one hour and, at a later Forecast time, the next Color is tonated, and so on.

2-A. COLORS. The original Spectro-Chrome system used five matched glass slides (filters which were not monochromes) to produce 12 Colors. Dinshah used the term **Attuned Colors** to differentiate them from filters which appeared to be the same but were not necessarily correct Color shades for Spectro-Chrome use. The five attuned slides were used in this manner:

Spectro-Chrome Color:		Slides used:			
RED	–	Red	‖ BLUE	–	Blue
ORANGE	–	Red and Yellow	‖ INDIGO	–	Blue and Violet
YELLOW	–	Yellow	‖ VIOLET	–	Violet
LEMON	–	Yellow and Green	‖ PURPLE	–	Violet and Yellow
GREEN	–	Green	‖ MAGENTA	–	Red and Violet
TURQUOISE	–	Green and Blue	‖ SCARLET	–	Red and Blue

2-B. The required Colors also can be made by other means (see Chapter Three, Spectro-Chrome Color Production).

2-C. In an emergency, any means of approximating a Color can be used; that would be Color therapy but not necessarily Spectro-Chrome therapy. Spectro-Chrome Colors have certain constituents besides the obvious as explained in Chapter three.

3. AREA. The part of the body you are going to tonate is called an AREA. The areas are numbered from #1 through #22, and approximately contain the major organs:

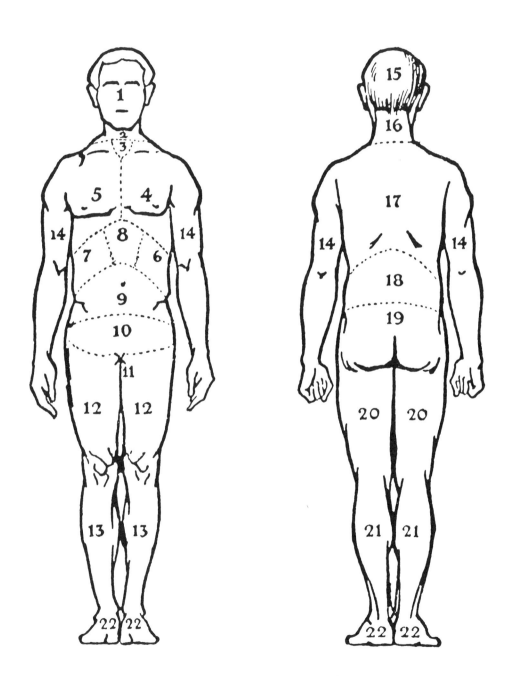

Area #

- 1 – Pituitary, pineal, brain (front)
- 2 – Neck
- 3 – Thyroid, parathyroids
- 4, 5 – Lungs, heart, thymus (directly below area #3), (female – mammaries)
- 6 – Spleen
- 7 – Liver (also area #8), gall bladder
- 8 – Stomach (also area 6), pancreas (front)
- 9 – Intestines (also area 10)
- 10 – Bladder, appendix, internal reproductive
- 11 – External reproductive
- 12 – Thighs
- 13 – Shins
- 14 – Arms
- 15 – Brain (back)
- 15 to 19 – Spine, spinal cord
- 16 – Nape of neck
- 17 – Lungs (back)
- 18 – Kidneys, adrenals, pancreas (back)
- 19 – Rectum, buttocks
- 20 – Back of thighs
- 21 – Calves
- 22 – Feet

4. SYSTEMIC (front or back). The term SYSTEMIC FRONT means to tonate all areas from #1 through #11 (unless directed to give the tonation over the entire front of the body from the soles of the feet, area #22). SYSTEMIC BACK means to tonate all areas from #15 through #19 (unless directed to tonate the entire back of the body from the soles of the feet, area #22).

5. PROJECTOR. The filters can be used with almost any incandescent lamp (or Sunlight) as a Light source or projector; fluorescent tubes are not suitable for generating Spectro-Chrome Colors (see Chapter three, Color Production).

6. INFRA-GREEN, ULTRA-GREEN. Red, Orange, Yellow, and Lemon are Colors which occur in the spectrum before Green, the center Color, so they are termed INFRA-GREEN Colors, and tend to be stimulating. Turquoise, Blue, Indigo, and Violet are Colors which are found in the spectrum after Green so they are termed ULTRA-GREEN Colors, and tend to be depressants. Green, in the middle, is the physical equilibrating Color. Purple, Magenta, and Scarlet are not found in the spectrum so they are not included in either series.

7-A. OPPOSITE. Each Spectro-Chrome Color has specific effects attributed to it (see Chapter six). The Color which has reverse attributes of another Color is called its OPPOSITE in this book. In Dinshah's writings the same meaning was given to the word "affinity" but we feel "opposite" gives a clearer understanding.   Each line of the following list is to be read both ways, Red is the OPPOSITE of Blue so it follows that Blue generally gives the OPPOSITE effects of Red, and so on:

Red	–	Blue
Orange	–	Indigo
Yellow	–	Violet
Lemon	–	Turquoise
Purple	–	Scarlet

If a particular area is stimulated by Yellow then it would tend to be depressed by Violet; if an area is stimulated by Indigo then it would tend to be depressed by Orange and so on.

7-B. The remaining Colors, Green and Magenta, do not have opposite Colors. Green is the median Color of the spectrum and is therefore the Governing Color (physical, positive polarity). Magenta is the simultaneous use of both ends of the spectrum which endows it with the power of equilibration (emotional, negative polarity). Dinshah termed them dual aspects of the same frequency.

7-C. Lemon and Turquoise are OPPOSITE Colors in some respects, but due to their each containing ½ of the Governor Green they have a similarity in their ability to cause favorable changes in nutrition and tissue repair. Generally, Lemon is used in chronic cases, Turquoise for acute conditions.

8-A. AURA. The energy field surrounding and extending from the physical body, generated by the electro-chemical cellular activity of the body is called the AURA in the Spectro-Chrome system. The aura diminishes rapidly as the distance from the body increases so tonations must be on bare skin.

8-B. Color therapy acts by reinforcement or interference of the aura. Any illness, pain, infection, attack, shock, breakdown, or other untoward occurrence, will result in a change in the (invisible) Color of the aura or alter its strength. If the change is a weakening of the aura in a particular area, tonate with the Color necessary to reinforce the aura of that area. On the other hand, if the change causes as excess of activity in an area with a resulting increase of auric energy, tonate with the opposite Color as illustrated in paragraph 7-A. Appropriate Colors for each area are listed in Chapter six, Tonations by Symptoms.

9-A. VARIANT BREATH FORECAST. In a manner similar to the tides of the seas, there are "tides" several times each day within the human body when the bodily forces are more receptive to the influence of Color therapy. This "tides" phenomenon is evidenced by the left and right nostrils breathing in a pattern of varying pressure and is predictable, hence the term VARIANT BREATH FORE-CAST. Since the Forecast is based on Sunrise, Sunset, and New Moon date, it changes each year and with location.

9-B. Each Forecast time (starting time for a one-hour tonation) is calculated to be when a particular nostril is (or should be) near its minimum pressure. At the end of the one-hour tonation, the nostril which was at minimum pressure will (or should) be at or exceed the pressure of the other nostril. The point at which the nostrils are equal in pressure is called the "junction" and is the most important part of a tonation. The junction occurs well after the middle of a one-hour tonation so it is advisable, if a shortened tonation is unavoidable, to begin the tonation late rather than end it early.

9-C. A nostril breathes from a minimum pressure to a maximum and back again to minimum in two hours and 56 minutes; at the same time, the other nostril is going in reverse manner: maximum to minimum to maximum. Nostril pressures can be controlled and even reversed if necessary, but doing so without good reason can be harmful. The beginning of each Forecast time is two hours and 56 minutes from the beginning of the last Forecast time because a tonation time always starts when one nostril is at minimum pressure and the other at maximum. The factor for determining which nostril should be at minimum is the Lunar cycle: left nostril for the first 15 days after New Moon, right nostril for the balance of the cycle. This is probably more than you wanted to know but it may help to impress on you the importance of using the Forecast times for tonations when possible. Spectro-Chrome often works well even without this "little detail" but at least keep it in mind because you may encounter a condition where it may make the difference between success and failure.

9-D. Besides the preferred times for beginning tonations, the Forecast sheets list New Moon and Full Moon dates, and eclipse dates and times; they are provided because serious health conditions may require greater attention around those dates, and tonations should not be given during an eclipse. The Forecast is published annually by the Dinshah Health Society for its members (a membership application form is included at the end of this book).

10. ACUTE or CHRONIC. The terms ACUTE (or recent) and CHRONIC (or long standing) do not necessarily relate to the duration of the condition. Acute conditions often generate a rise in bodily temperature (fever) while chronic ailments tend to have little or no fever. The person's temperature is used as a guide whether the problem is to be considered acute or chronic. In general, acute cases use tonations of ultra-Green Colors, and chronic cases require infra-Green tonations.

11. The RATIO. The equation of heart rate divided by respiration rate (one inhalation/exhalation is one respiration count) gives the RATIO. For example, if the heart rate is 75 with a respiration 15, the ratio is five (75 divided by 15 is five). Chapter five, Technique, has details on how to use the ratio.

12. ATTRIBUTE. The Spectro-Chrome system uses 12 Colors each of which has more than one specific tonation purpose. Each of these characteristics is termed an ATTRIBUTE. Chapter six catalogs 78 attributes, and how to use them without a differential diagnosis in many conditions.

13-A. COLOR SCHEDULES. Chapter seven of this book has 327 Color schedules listing tonations for over 400 health conditions, but to use them properly Spectro-Chrome technique must be used. In this Chapter and the next four, there are 32 pages. Whether these 32 pages, with other available material, are enough to teach you how to use this System effectively and with confidence is entirely up to you. Some have picked up this book, looked in the index for the Color Schedule pertaining to their particular problem and proceeded. That is one way but it is certainly far from the best way.

13-B. Humanity is heir to thousands of diagnosable disorders. Learning to treat them by orthodox methods takes many years of arduous effort. While these 32 pages of course cannot teach surgery, emergency procedures and other highly technical matters, most people can learn how to use Spectro-Chrome competently if a conscientious effort is made. Re-read the 32 pages until well familiarized.

13-C. The Color schedules cover hundreds of the more common illnesses, and if you use ALL the information available in this book, many unlisted conditions also can be tonated. The Color Schedules should be a part of the learning process rather than the sole use of this book. Additionally, you will have the opportunity to benefit from the potential inherent in Spectro-Chrome to work on conditions of which you may not even be aware.

14. NORMALATE. Dinshah did not use the word "cure" in relation to Spectro-Chrome. While his coined term "normalate" has some of the meaning of cure, in a larger sense it means something quite different. People are built in approximately the same mold with a heart, lungs, skin, teeth, etc., but how **your** organs function as a whole can vary considerably compared to the medically accepted norm and still be satisfactory for you. Spectro-Chrome is not expected to change the genetic factors which play such an important part in good or poor health, but it can minimize the "side-effects" some of those factors cause, thereby helping you to become what is normal for **you**: NORMALATE you.

15. You will be repaid many times over for your effort and diligence in learning to use this System as it was designed, thereby becoming more responsible for your own health care and able to do more about it.

*   *   *   *   *

CHAPTER THREE

SPECTRO-CHROME COLOR PRODUCTION

A-1. FILTERS. Dinshah designed his original Color system with five glass slides (filters). For many years he resisted using the term "filters", and propounded his own theory of Light; he later conformed with present scientific thought. There was nothing special or secret in the glass he used as filters. It was purchased from commercial suppliers, and then each set of five Color slides was matched (attuned) to meet Dinshah's standards. It may sound simple but the attuning process was often a frustrating task due to the inconsistencies in the glass; attuning is an art rather than a science. Sometimes more than three-quarters of a shipment could not be matched into sets meeting Spectro-Chrome requirements.

A-2. Almost any Colors can be used for "Color therapy", but there are reasons why Spectro-Chrome Colors are not and can not be monochromes or "just any Colors". In the original method, five filters were employed singly and also in combinations to produce secondary and tertiary Colors. Therefore, each of the five basic filters had to be a polychrome of suitable proportions in order to generate appropriate Colors when used in the requisite combinations. They are also necessarily broad-spectrum filters, each with a preponderance of its prime frequency (Color), to give an effect at least somewhat similar to that of Fraunhofer Lines. (The concept behind the connection of Spectro-Chrome and Fraunhofer emission/absorption Lines is explained in Chapter nine.) It now should be evident why it is difficult to find suitable glass filters.

A-3. One method to entirely eliminate the filter problem is to utilize a prism or diffraction grating. Dinshah designed, but never completed, a "slideless" Color projector which would have offered an array of 72 Colors (six gradations for each of the 12 Spectro-Chrome Colors). A prism resolves white Light into a complete spectrum; combining appropriate parts of the spectrum would then produce ideal Spectro-Chrome Colors. Unfortunately, this is much easier said than done. A $3000 commercial unit was tested by us some years ago and found to be inadequate for our purposes (poor Color resolution).

A-4. Professional spectrum projectors have been available for decades, used by those interested in Light for other purposes such as in the photographic field. The price of suitable devices, however, puts them beyond the reach of most people. Furthermore, there is no assurance they would give better results than the relatively simple Spectro-Chrome projectors in use since 1920. Glass filters must be matched, prism projectors are too expensive – if you are to use Spectro-Chrome therapy, how will you proceed? Let us suggest some ways.

A-5. Despite the mistaken assumption of some people that the original filters had unique intrinsic healing properties, they were only a means to an end: removing specific parts from the complete spectrum of white Light by the use of appropriate glass filters. Our present-day alternative method to the same end is equally productive, in some respects superior, and easily obtainable. It is a set of Roscolene filters, manufactured by Rosco Laboratories. Because some theatrical filter dealers do not sell many Roscolene filters, their stock may be outdated for our purposes. To avoid any such pitfalls, contact this well-stocked dealer which is aware of all the filter numbers needed: Samarco Inc., P O Box 153008, Dallas TX 75315-3008 USA, phone 214 421-0757. We have also recommended other filter brands years ago but no longer do so because of the difficulty in keeping track of changing tints and Color values. As it is, when Rosco alters the formulation of a filter we are using (which is infrequent), we may have to change the recommendations for any Spectro-Chrome Colors affected thereby. If you purchased this book directly from Dinshah Health Society, any filter changes required since its publication would be noted in the space below. If purchased from a bookstore (which may have had it in stock for some time), even if there is a notation it may have been superseded; send a self-addressed envelope to Dinshah Health Society for possible later changes. Relying on others is certainly not an ideal situation but it does help to keep the Spectro-Chrome System alive and functioning.

A-6. We are presently using nine filters (or eleven, see paragraph A-8); the number is larger than needed for glass filters because we have been unable to find filters in the same Color densities as the glass. The methodology is different but the result is the same–Spectro-Chrome Colors. Order these Roscolene filter numbers: 809, 810, 818, 828, 832, 859, 861, 866, 871 (826, 877, see para. A-8). When you receive the Roscolene sheets be sure their numbers agree with the foregoing list (do not allow substitutions), and carefully mark each one with its Roscolene number. Pay no attention to the theatrical names given by the manufacturer–rose pink–straw–surprise blue–etc. as they mean nothing to us. (Already assembled filter sets may be available from Samarco.) It is immaterial which filter is placed ahead or behind another for Colors using two or three filters. Use their numbers to assemble them in this manner:

S-C Color:	Filter number(s):			
RED	– 818, 828	‖	ORANGE	– 809, 828
YELLOW	– 809	‖	LEMON	– 809, 871
GREEN	– 871	‖	TURQUOISE	– 861, 871
BLUE	– 859, 866	‖	INDIGO	– 828, 859, 866
VIOLET	– 832, 859, 866	‖	PURPLE	– 832, 866
MAGENTA	– 818, 828, 866	‖	SCARLET	– 810, 818, 861

A-7. The sheets are 20x24" and can be cut with a scissors to suit your needs. The Roscolene filters, when put together in this manner, approximate the original glass filters. They are not ideal any more than the glass was; they are a good commercial version of Spectro-Chrome Colors just as the glass was. Glass can crack if overheated, plastic filters can fade if overheated, so they are about even on that score. Five glass slides were used for a set; Roscolene filters require nine for the reason stated above, a minor disadvantage for plastic but on the plus side there is the availability of in-between Colors if you wish to use them (para. A-8). These differences are obviously of no real consequence in the successful application of Spectro-Chrome. There is every reason to expect the Roscolene filters to give the same results as glass, and 17 years' use (to 1997) unequivocally bears out this presumption. While perfection is rarely seen on Earth, and we have no hesitancy in recommending these filters, rest assured we will continue to seek filters coming as close as possible to ideal Spectro-Chrome Colors.

A-8. Paragraph A-3 describes a projector Dinshah designed to give 72 Color gradations. The intent was to give a practitioner recourse when a patient said that a particular tonation Color was "too strong." If, say, Orange seemed too powerful for a given case but Yellow might not have enough "kick", then a Color between them could be selected. At the moment we can offer five "in-between" Colors; they are not mentioned elsewhere or used in this book but are listed to allow those so inclined the opportunity to test them. In some instances, an in-between Color induces a response superior to standard Spectro-Chrome Colors but this is likely to be the exception rather than the rule. That Dinshah was aware of their value is demonstrated by his quest for the 72-Color projector. The Color names explain themselves: RED-ORANGE is a Color between Red and Orange, etc. Order two additional Roscolene filters (#826 and 877) to make:

RED-ORANGE	809, 818	‖	ORANGE-YELLOW	809, 826
LEMON-GREEN	810, 871	‖	GREEN-TURQUOISE	871, 877
TURQUOISE-BLUE	859, 877	‖		

A-9. If the filters will be used with a focussed Light source such as a 35-mm slide projector, it is recommended that the front lens tube be removed and the filters be placed/hung/clipped/taped to the front of the equipment instead of using the customary slide position in the middle of the projector which is much closer to the bulb. A test of filters used in this way with a 300-watt device showed no fading after five years of intermittent use which suggests Roscolene filters will last indefinitely if not overheated. A fluorescent tube runs at a much lower temperature but is not suitable as a Spectro-Chrome Light source because it emits a considerably different spectrum compared to an incandescent bulb. Further, all fluorescent lamps emit Fraunhofer Lines which would be unacceptable during tonations; our **My Spectro-Chrome** video has a demonstration of these emissions, as well as short-comings of so-called "full-spectrum" neodymium bulbs.

A-10. For those Colors produced by combining two or three filters: Assemble the required filters for each Color and tape or staple the edges together of each filter set. Make "name-tags" on pieces of masking tape, one for each Color, and place on a corner of the respective Colors to avoid the possibility of errors.

A-11. Page 310 (page 67, 3rd edition) of Dinshah's **Spectro-Chrome Metry Encyclopedia** states: "You will note, that in any combination, two slides [filters] are used; at no time are three combined." That statement does not hold true for the presently used Roscolene filters because the same Color densities as the original glass filters are not available. It can be readily seen with a spectroscope that there is a progressive reduction of frequencies (Colors) as each filter is added, so when three filters are required that is what will be listed. Glass or plastic: somewhat different techniques giving the same results, and it is of course the results which count.

B-1. LIGHT SOURCES. The most often asked question is, "Will a more powerful bulb work better?" The answer for all intents and purposes is NO. Everything from a lantern to Sunlight, which is thousands of times brighter, has been used with equally gratifying results. A thorough evaluation of the subject is in Chapter four, Five Thousand Pages, paragraph A. Do not be overly concerned about Light source power; use anything convenient, such as:

B-2. SUNLIGHT. The Roscolene filters are large enough (20x24") to cover a window. This is of somewhat limited practicality for tonating as the Sun must be shining, the angle of the rays must be such as to allow sitting or lying near the window (the Sun's rays must be used, not sky-light), and night tonations are obviously impossible. Even with these shortcomings, the method has been successfully employed, and is valuable in areas without electricity. If the weather permits, a tonation can be taken outdoors by simply exposing the necessary area and covering it with the appropriate filters; eyes should be closed except if the tonation is on area #1. Of course, there could be a problem with privacy, depending on the area being tonated and how close is your nearest neighbor. There may be some lessening of the desired effect due to Sunlight penetrating clothing on other areas, and area #1 being exposed.

B-3. A FLASHLIGHT. This is very similar to an outdoor tonation but the weather is no longer a consideration. It can be used in a cool room for a very localized tonation: expose the tonation area, place the filter on the area and position the lit flashlight on the filter, then cover the person with a blanket. An alternative method is to tape the filters to the face of the flashlight which allows a wider coverage by moving it away from the tonation area, but a systemic tonation may be difficult to achieve and the lower limit of effective tonation illumination may be passed. Rotating the use of two sets of rechargeable batteries can be used to lessen the expense.

B-4. A SLIDE PROJECTOR. These are widely available and with a few modifications make suitable Light sources, except for their usually narrow beam which may make systemic tonations difficult. Projector bulbs are run excessively luminous to give a brilliant image on the screen; their life expectancy is typically quite short. The bulb can be made to run much cooler and last far longer by installing a high-current diode in series with the bulb (but not in the cooling fan circuit). Diodes (solid-state rectifiers) are available from electronic suppliers, TV repair shops, etc. Use a diode of about twice the amperage rating of the bulb; a 120-volt 300-watt bulb should have a 6-ampere diode. Some projectors can use a "detuned" (somewhat dimmer) bulb which lasts much longer and does not need the diode; ask your local photographic supply dealer if one is available for your model projector. Some projectors emit too much Light into the room so baffles (made of cardboard?) on the openings may be required. A drilled and tapped ¼x20-thread in the base of the projector will permit the use of a camera tripod for convenience in adjusting the Light beam on the patient. Do not put the filters into the projector where the slides would normally be inserted; follow the directions in the preceding section, Filters, paragraph A-9. Another type of projector is a "Best PAR-38 Can" (about $39) available from many theatrical filter suppliers. Lining most of its inside with aluminum foil is recommended (leave the back unlined for ventilation). Use a 60-watt standard household type bulb in it.

B-5. ANYTHING. It means just that: <u>ANYTHING.</u> How about an automobile headlight with a battery or transformer, or a pole-lamp with the filters taped on, or a small box with a small spotlight in it (may require air-vent holes or a small fan for cooling)? Or a table lamp – cut a hole in the front of the shade and tape on the filters – cover the rest of the shade with dark paper so the room will not be illuminated, leaving a few small spaces to cool the lamp. You can make a simple and practical projector which gives excellent coverage for systemic tonations by using a 60-watt reflector lamp (about $7), some glue and tape and cardboard, and the set of plans in Chapter 14; hundreds have been built and used successfully. Use your imagination to GET GOING, but *DO GET GOING!*

CHAPTER FOUR

FIVE THOUSAND PAGES

1. From June 1922 through November 1947 Dinshah edited the Spectro-Chrome magazine (and Visible Spectrum Researcher, 1955-57). It initially encompassed many more subjects than the title indicated. There were 12 sections, one heading for each Spectro-Chrome Color (each issue may have had three or four of these sections): Red – Dinshah editorials; Orange – humor, wit; Yellow – inquiry, catechism; Lemon – other healing methods, science; Green – Spectro-Chrome therapy; Turquoise – poetry, art; Blue – history, geography; Indigo – (no heading found); Violet – metaphysics, psychology; Purple – politics, royalty; Magenta – love, friendship; Scarlet – (no heading found).

2. As interest in Spectro-Chrome increased, the sectioned format was dropped and Spectro-Chrome therapy eventually became almost the sole subject. The magazines spanned over 6000 pages in those 29 years, and while the case reports were somewhat repetitious, there were editorial remarks by Dinshah revealing technique and details about Spectro-Chrome not found in any other writings.

3. After losing a federal trial in 1947-48 (pertaining to Food and Drug Administration regulations), Dinshah was placed on five-years probation. One probation requirement was that he surrender all material in his possession pertaining to Spectro-Chrome for destruction in the Camden NJ incinerator. He was allowed to keep one set of magazines and other writings for his personal library. Except for the few copies which surfaced from time-to-time, Spectro-Chrome magazines were out-of-print for decades. With the wealth of information in these booklets, Dinshah Health Society re-published them in 1990 (by photocopy process) in a seven volume set.

4. The following paragraphs are prompted by material in the magazines, with rewording and commentary by me. Some of the paragraphs answer often-asked questions; some is argumentative and you may draw your own conclusions. Numbers in parentheses are magazine page references.

A-1. BULB WATTAGE (94, 332, 1870, 1966, 2026, 3747, 3896). In the early years of Spectro-Chrome practice, Dinshah sold 100-watt projectors (standard model) as well as larger units, and received continuing accounts of successful use in all types of ailments. In several instances, O.H.F. reported using the standard projector for serious illnesses. Included were his mother (age 66, intestinal disorder of more than five-years standing) and an aunt (age 70, bronchitis for 40 years, skin problem for 20 years); both cases gained good health within a month. Dinshah commented, "[O.H.F.] is not a professional Spectro-Chrome Therapist. Yet the satisfactory results obtained by him could be obtained by any person using Spectro-Chrome Therapy as per instructions laid down. O.F. achieved the results with a 100-watt equipment, which speaks well for his intelligent application." In later years, however, Dinshah decried its use for anything but minor problems. In 1936 he marketed a 400-watt unit with the express understanding that even with this 4-times greater wattage it should be used only on acute cases. Nonetheless, it appears that it is basically the quality and not the quantity of Light which generates the effect. People have used anything from a

4 1/2-watt nightlight (Dinshah treated his first patient with Color in 1897 by the filtered rays of a kerosene lantern) to a 2000-watt Graduate model Spectro-Chrome equipment, with equally gratifying results.

A-2. Further, Dinshah wrote, "Magenta being a very dark [Color] wave, does not appeal so much by its visibility. Study will show that while Yellow is visible 1000, Violet [which is ½ in Magenta] is only six. Effect has nothing to do with sight." So, here he said that even though Yellow is 165-times brighter than Violet, the auric effects are the same – it does not matter what you see: "Effect has nothing to do with sight." If Yellow and other bright Colors were more effective than Magenta because of their luminosity, they would hit like a hammer while Magenta and other dark Colors would be relatively impotent. In practice, ANY Color can cause an energetic reaction if it is the particular one strongly needed by that person at that time, and this is so regardless of the brilliance of the Color being tonated.

A-3. Another view of the subject: People have used the Sun as their Light source for tonating. A typical value for Sunlight at noon is about 10,000-foot-candles while a 300-watt slide projector (with a diode in the bulb circuit) may give 100-foot-candles at a tonation distance of 3½-feet. 300 watts or the Sun, they give the same results; if intense illumination were the prime necessity for best results then the "Sun-projector" with its 100-times greater luminescence than the 300-watter would be far more effective. Carry this one step further and consider a Yellow tonation with the Sun versus a Magenta tonation with our typical 300-watt projector: the difference in tonation illumination is enormous but the effect is equal. We will say it one more time: the results achievable with Spectro-Chrome do not depend on using a powerful Light source.

A-4. Psychologic effect is important in any healing method so Dinshah may have been reassuring users with higher-powered projectors because they made the darker Colors more visible when tonated. We are not aware of any tests to determine the minimum effective Light level but there must be some limit. For example, it would not be reasonable to take a tonation with a candle a mile away. The weight of thought here says to put your mind at ease and use whatever Light source is available or convenient.

A-5. One more point to consider is the additional effect of Light energy entering through the eyes. Much research has focused on this facet with very little on how it is utilized through the aura. Some interesting articles: Light and Your Health, **Popular Science** of February 1969, page 78 et seq.; The Effects of Light on the Human Body, **Scientific American** of July 1975, page 69 et seq.; Startling New Theories on Light and Color, **Popular Mechanics** of September 1978, page 81 et seq. The last listed article included a section on kinesiology with Color therapy. Dinshah's work was mentioned but left the impression that there was no continuation of it after his death which is obviously incorrect.

B. KINESIOLOGY (32). A French experimenter, Dr. Fere, noted in 1922 that a person's hand-grip was strongest under Red Light and diminished as the Color went across the spectrum. This phenomenon is used by some kinesiologists and can be easily demonstrated, but it is now realized that in some people a Color other than Red may help develop a stronger grip (or in other muscles) due to the person's auric necessities at that time.

C. THE RATIO (2390, 2662, 3036, 4754).   The ratio between the heart rate and respiration rate is vitally important in Spectro-Chrome therapy; many disorders cannot be tonated effectively without determining the ratio and taking appropriate steps to correct it if faulty. After determining the ratio, how to utilize it is in Chapter five, Technique. In acute disorders, Magenta is often used to assure adequate oxygenation and circulation but when the ratio is incorrect then Purple (if high) or Scarlet (if low) may be indicated. Another condition which requires careful consideration of the ratio is a "dry cough" (non-productive of phlegm). It is not always from throat irritation; a heart disorder or heart/lung imbalance can be responsible so Purple, Magenta or Scarlet may be required according to ratio indications (if in doubt, try Purple as it is usually beneficial for a dry cough). The same rules apply for bleeding in the lungs.

D. ANIMALS (139, 911, 2707, 3514).   There is no reason why animals, birds, or any living creature can not be successfully tonated. Their anatomy may be different from human but they have the same type of emanations due to cellular activity as we do. The difficulty may lie in determining what problem the "patient" has. Generally, Chapter six, Tonations by Symptoms, can help. An Itisometer could be an aid if the creature is not so large that internal temperatures could not be measured accurately; fur or feathers would be a further handicap to a reliable evaluation.

E. P/M/S SYSTEMIC (346, 634, 697, 746).   Reading later-years Spectro-Chrome magazine reports gives the impression that Purple, Magenta, and Scarlet tonations are used almost exclusively on areas #4-5-18 for affecting the heart and circulation. Such local tonations are still recommended for many conditions, but experience as well as several references leads us to insist that there are times when the tonations MUST be systemic before satisfactory results will be attained. Further, in a few cases (allergy, high blood pressure,) the desired effect was not achieved until the tonations were arranged to include the entire body, all the way from the soles of the feet (from area #22 through area #1). The production and utilization of renin/norepinephrine/epinephrine is a complex arrangement for controlling heart-rate/blood pressure, etc., and in part is carried out all through the body. It is therefore easy to understand why SYSTEMIC Purple, Magenta or Scarlet tonations (or other Colors in some cases) may be essential.

F-1. ITISOMETER (343, 773, 785, 3228, 3429).   The Itisometer was designed in 1923 and marketed in early 1925 (patent 8/29, #1,724,469); from then until production ceased in 1942, 44 were hand-made which led to a $425 price. The Itisometer was essentially a sensitive electric thermometer (using a modified Wheatstone's-bridge circuit). When its sensing element (Tanger) was applied to the bare skin in turn over each vital organ, the main dial registered which areas were or were not normal in temperature for that person. That is the essence of Itisometry but the actual technique is considerably more complex.

F-2. To allow for differences in personal metabolism, a measurement session (Itisation) was begun by taking temperature readings at five point on the person's head. An average of the five was determined with the "Auriculator" device on the Itisometer. The Itisation proceeds by measuring and listing the skin temperature over each vital organ. These are then averaged on the Auriculator, using the head-reading average as a metabolic adjustment factor. The "Ratio Dial" of the Auriculator now indicates the Colors to tonate. If a listing showed a local area in need of a Color markedly different from the systemic Colors, local tonations were indicated. A more sophisticated use of the information obtained was to use the table of Color Attributes. For example, if area seven were somewhat underactive the Itisometer may have suggested tonations of Lemon or, depending on the level of underactivity, Yellow, Orange, Red. However, to take more direct action, the Table of Color Attributes in Chapter six says, "Red, liver energizer, areas #7-8"; or if overactivity were the case, the opposite Color could be used: Blue. The Itisometer had no provision for indicating circulatory Colors (Purple, Magenta, Scarlet) so judgement had to be exercised in their use.

F-3. Dinshah gave courses on Itisometer technique, and post-graduate lectures helped explain Itisometer quirks mentioned in the Spectro-Chrome magazines (their nature was not always reported). In one instance, seemingly completely at odds with Spectro-Chrome teachings, the Itisometer indicated the need for Red tonations on a patient's badly inflamed eyes. The physician was reluctant to follow the recommendation but having confidence in Dinshah's Itisometer eventually did so. The effect astonished her and the patient: three Red tonations alleviated the congestion and pain. The reason for this seeming inconsistency was the failure of the practitioner to first determine the pulse/breathing RATIO which should have shown a need for an increase in blood circulation. Red, a component in both Scarlet and Magenta (circulatory Colors), took their place for increasing circulation. There is an answer for every question but it is not always readily apparent. This also illustrates another magnificent feature of Spectro-Chrome: The exact Color is not always essential for results as is explained in Chapter six, paragraph two.

F-4. The patent on the Itisometer only describes its general construction without giving electrical constants or Color/temperature equivalents. A modern electronic thermometer (about $700) can be used by converting its numerical readings to Itisometer values with a set of charts. These are available in an updated Itisometer Manual from Dinshah Health Society.

G. STRONG REACTIONS (724, 1526, 1943, 2723, 3481, 3896, 4990). If the recommended technique for beginning a series of tonations is not followed (and sometimes even when it is), a strong physical reaction may be experienced. When any Color is "upsetting" to the patient, stop the tonation and consider:

1. Green systemic front to activate the body's governing system.

2. Magenta on areas #4-5-18 to be sure blood circulation is normalated (also, re-check the pulse/respiration ratio, Chapter five, Technique).

3. If Magenta causes discomfort, resume the tonation with Purple. It is permissible to change one Color step during a tonation rather than wait for the next Forecast time; e.g., when tonating Yellow – change to either Orange or Lemon, or an in-between Color next to Yellow (if one is available).

4. Yellow systemic front to be sure eliminations are adequate, and energize the lymphatic system.

5. If the person is still overly sensitive to tonations after using appropriate paragraphs above, the eyes may be covered during the tonation, and/or shorten the tonation time (see Chapter two, paragraph 9-B, for abbreviating tonations without missing the Forecast junction).

H. TWO-COLOR TONATIONS (234, 698, 907, 1921, 2022, 3536, 4086, 4476). When circumstances indicate that time is of the essence, there is a procedure for using two Color projectors simultaneously with the same or different Colors. In some cases with a high fever, or when the condition requires front and back tonations, these instructions should be followed carefully:

1. Use two Colors from the same side of the spectrum in one tonation. Any two of these Colors may be tonated:

    Red, Orange, Yellow, Lemon, Green. Or any two of these:

    Green, Turquoise, Blue, Indigo, Violet. Or:

    Magenta and Purple. Or:

    Magenta and Scarlet.

2. Tonate one Color on front areas or systemic, and the other Color on back areas or systemic; their rays must not overlap on the person's body.

3. When different Colors are tonated, the patient's eyes should be kept closed (or covered) to avoid accentuating one Color's effect over the other.

4. Both projectors should be turned on at a Forecast time and turned off one hour later, except:

5. If a recent condition is being tonated, it is sometimes helpful or necessary to use an extended or even a continuous tonation until satisfactory progress is noted (a high fever is controlled, itching from poison ivy does not return when the tonation is stopped, and so on). In such cases the body's defense forces are hard at work and can receive and utilize more Color energy. This usually does not hold true in long-standing (chronic) cases so it is recommended that tonations be limited to two one-hour sessions per day.

I-1. SLOW or NO RESULTS (772, 848, 871, 1505, 2095, 2188, 2465, 2922, 3097, 3249, 3406, 3866, 3896, 3897, 4421, 5011). It must be admitted that Spectro-Chrome (or any healing method for that matter) does not always give the results expected of it. Reasons for some failures are readily apparent, in others they are not. Some possibilities are:

I-2. <u>Poor Diet.</u> It seems everybody knows someone who lived on "beef, booze, and tobacco" to age 98, but by-and-large humans (especially sick ones) do better on a well-balanced vegetarian diet, without alcohol or tobacco in any form. Some people have had good results with Spectro-Chrome no matter what they did, but when instructions are not followed its capabilities obviously are less likely to be fully realized.

I-3. <u>Lack of Persistence.</u> Some cases may take a considerable time for progress to be apparent. E.S. reported tonating her mother (paralysis after a stroke) usually with two tonations a day for two years before she was well. (This is quoted for length of time, not for lack of results, as she was delighted from the very first tonation.) Dinshah warned against giving an interested person "a few tonations" to convince them, because some chronic conditions may not respond quickly. There are some intractable conditions which require significant persistence. That was his feeling but since most people experience at least some results promptly, it may be worth the risk.

I-4. <u>Incorrect Technique.</u>   A woman complained of "no results" after a month of tonations. Careful inquiry revealed she insisted on tonating with a bed-sheet covering herself so her husband would not see her nude. Observing Forecast tonation times is essential in some cases. Following the recommended technique assures that all that can be done will be done in as short a time as possible.

I-5. Too Late. Sooner or later a time comes when a person's bodily reparative efforts cannot keep up with the ever-present balancing destructive forces; death is then inevitable unless either the constructive forces can be adequately stimulated or the destructive factors abated. If neither of these can be accomplished quickly enough, it is then a terminal case, or Too Late. Foretelling whether a disorder is a lost cause is often difficult or incorrect. Even if a dire prediction is accurate, much comfort may be secured by continuing with the tonations. Besides, the inevitable can be postponed and "miracles" have been known to happen.

I-6. Hidden Causes. It is now widely recognized that many ailments have their roots in stressful living, emotional turmoil, or other difficult-to-pin-down causes. If the cause is not found and corrected, recovery is bound to be retarded and recurrence is likely after tonations are discontinued. Many decades ago Dinshah suggested the possibility of mercury-based dental fillings causing obscure problems; there is presently much support to this theory, and certainly could be classified as a "hidden cause". Further, it is well to consider the Biblical passage in St. John, 9:2-3; that the follies of parents are seen in their children. Heredity takes a share of responsibility in hidden causes. Mental attitude, which includes religious faith, can play a very important part in the course of any disorder. Worry, in the usual sense, gains little; mature concern with positive action will bear fruit. Spectro-Chrome can be and has been efficacious whether the person believed in it or not, and even with unconscious persons. But, there is every reason to expect it to work best when the patient maintains a positive attitude; it may be termed The Will to Live, and can be a vital part of all therapies.

I-7. Other Help Necessary. If only one healing method were available, it should be Spectro-Chrome as it follows most closely the dictum, "Above all, do thy patient no harm". There are times, however, when it is indeed fortunate that other modalities are at hand. Reconstructive surgery for birth-defects, reattaching a severed part after an accident, suturing an eye-injury with thread so fine it floats away if not kept moist – are some examples of amazing technical skill. It may be helpful to lance an abscess on the sole of the foot where the skin is too thick to allow pus to drain. But, in all these instances Spectro-Chrome can be relied on to hasten healing, reduce likelihood of infection, lessen scarring, and in general make patients more comfortable.

I-8. Expectations. Spectro-Chrome has the potential for affecting almost all health conditions, with the results dependent for the most part on each person's constitution. There are, nonetheless, a few conditions which have a low expectancy of an entirely successful outcome: Hardened granulations of the eye, reducing tumors beyond a certain point, fully developed cataracts, large kidney stones, the previously mentioned abscess, long-standing nerve problems, hernias in adults, are found in the magazines. A remarkably short list.

I-9. It Knows Best. What knows best? Why, your body of course! For instance, there is an unfounded fear of all fevers; "Oh my, Junior has a 99° fever, run and get the aspirin!" What a shame to thwart Nature's efforts. Fever is a friend not an enemy, unless it gets out of hand – above 104°F. or so. At elevated body temperatures the white blood-cell defenders fight more efficiently while most invading germs etc. multiply slower. Those are very good reasons not to fear a moderate fever. Spectro-Chrome does not eliminate fever, it works to remove the causative factors. Blue and Purple control high fevers without weakening the body's reparative powers.

I-10. <u>Chronic cases.</u> Some of these may be tonated for a considerable time without apparent results, especially when paralysis is involved, but it does not necessarily mean that nothing is happening inside. When the body is ready for effects to be noticeable, they will be. In some conditions, high blood pressure for instance, the symptom may be an indication of other problems, and lessening the pressure without taking the real cause into account is putting the cart before the horse. Spectro-Chrome may decrease blood pressure in a relatively short time to a level consistent with the demands of the body for adequate circulation but the underlying condition is likely to be chronic and take longer. As with all healing modalities Spectro-Chrome does have limitations, but even so it must be given a fair trial before abandoning it.

J-1. OUTSIDE INFLUENCES (1766, 1842, 1874, 2333, 3041, 3078, 3115, 3412, 3481, 4099). From birth until death we are surrounded by many influences, forces, energies, gravities, and undoubtedly by some of which are unknown as yet. Some people do not appear to be greatly influenced by these manifestations while others are markedly affected (especially when sick). If an attempt is made to avoid antagonism with at least some of these energies, less bodily energy will be needed to maintain or recover health. Some suggestions:

J-2. Tonations are best received while lying down with the head toward the North. Lying parallel with the Earth's magnetic field aligns the body's magnetic field with it, and as electricity flows at right angles to a magnetic field, it also aligns the electrical polarity (the liver and spleen). Lying on the stomach when tonating back areas is not advisable because that position reverses the electrical polarity in relation to the Earth (lie on the back or either side).

J-3. It is now documented that Moon phases are a factor in the moods of many people. If it is accepted that emotional and mental processes can be swayed, it should not be difficult to believe that the recommended Forecast times have value (Forecast times are calculated from New Moon day, and other factors). A correlation has been noted sometimes in New Moon and Full Moon days (and to a lesser extent for two days before and after them) with the crisis or turning point of a serious case. Extra vigilance should be exercised during those periods.

J-4. During a tonation, magnetic and electrical devices should be kept at least 18 inches from the person; this includes the projector if it uses a cooling fan. A distracting radio should not be playing. Under no circumstances should a television set be running in the tonation room; besides being distracting and emitting unwanted Light, they contain very high-voltage components.

J-5. In most inhabited areas of the World, clothing is required to prevent excessive body-heat loss. It wastes vitality to produce heat unnecessarily, and this extra effort may not be so well tolerated by a sick person. So, first, as the greatest heat loss occurs from the head, a loose-fitting cap should be worn at all times (well, almost all times); second, wear enough clothing to keep comfortably warm; third, the tonation room must be at least 80°F. for a systemic tonation.

There is usually little wisdom in taking a tonation for one problem and acquiring another in the process.

J-6. Considering the number of reputable researchers, dentists, etc., who believe there is a real and present threat in the continued use of mercury-based dental fillings, it would be prudent to consider a substitute. "Porcelain", epoxy, composite, or other alternative fillings may not be quite so durable as the amalgam but should be safer unless there is an allergy to some part of their composition. Dinshah believed the metallic fillings could produce minute electric currents which may lead to disorders of an obscure character.

J-7. Why it happens is not so important but when most people wear a watch on their left wrist, they are demonstrably weaker. Right wrist or carry a pocket watch (see Chapter 10, The Left Wristwatch).

K-1. LIMITATIONS (559, 848, 1382, 1505, 2922, 3097, 3531, 4174). We term the human electro-chemical emanation "the aura" though there is more than one aura. "The aura" is an exact reflection of the cellular activity within us, and in fact applies to all living matter. Spectro-Chrome basically does not act by penetration of tissues though this also may cause some effects. Its power results from reinforcement of weak auric areas and interference in areas of excessive activity. When the body or some part of it is tonated with Color energy, the aura can transmute and transmit this power to the cells which are generating the aura. A valid simile: Electricity energizing a coil of wire will produce magnetism in it; in reverse, moving a magnet through a coil of wire will induce a flow of electricity. Living cells produce the electrical energy, the aura is the energy radiating from the cells (in a sense, the wire), and in appropriate circumstances (as in a tonation) carries energy *to* the cells. A strong aura is evidence of vigorous cellular activity and is somewhat like a thicker wire which is able to carry more energy with fewer limitations.

K-2. One major difference between us and an electrical circuit is that we have inherent "governing" systems which tend to control or limit the utilization of Color energy while a wire will disintegrate if too much power is passed through it. This ability to reject unneeded Color potency is indeed fortunate (Providential?) for persons such as photo-darkroom operators who may spend many hours in Red or other unbalanced Light. Of course, protracted abuse of these remarkable innate defenses may eventually cause problems.

K-3. When there is vigorous cellular activity as in early and mid-life, the most may be expected from any healing system. For example, Spectro-Chrome is very useful on hernias up to the age of five but less so as age advances. Another interesting illustration: Reader's Digest magazine of March 1980 (page 62) described children under age 12 who had lost a fingertip to the crease of the first joint, and how regrowth took place – bone, flesh, skin, cuticle, finger nail – in about three months, but only if there were no surgical interference.

K-4. On limitations, Dinshah noted, "When age depreciates the auric vehicle, neither Spectro-Chrome nor anything else will produce the results he [the patient] is seeking in a persistent disorder of long standing. The inroads of age on the physical body can not be ignored, as we all have to die a physical death some day. Let him continue with Spectro-Chrome and watch his health." That Spectro-Chrome is effective at any age, at least to some degree, has been well documented through decades of use and thousands of cases, but to what extent in a specific instance depends in large measure on the person's constitution (their auric power). There are limits to how far you can turn back the clock.

K-5. The only cases cited are to illustrate particular points; two instances of successful use with a small projector on senior citizens may be noted in paragraph A-1. The following condensed quotation is particularly interesting for the last sentence of the second paragraph. Dr. K.B. reported on Mrs C. of fifty-some years of age, who had problems with her legs which recently had become "extremely painful with no relief day or night. About the middle of the thigh the internal saphenous vein of both legs was acutely inflamed. The legs up to just below the knees were swollen, intensely hard, just as hard as flesh could be. The deep as well as the superficial veins were involved and the color was best described as <u>black</u>. I have seen many and many bad legs, but for a pair with no skin broken these were the very worst. After the fifth treatment [tonation] the legs were soft, the swelling gone and the color good except for the actual veins which were now blue.

"Even with all the experience I have now had with Spectro-Chrome, I can hardly see how it was possible for any line of treatment to produce the results we had in these three cases [another leg problem similar to the one described, and one of otitis media]. When I first saw Mrs. C., I said to myself and to those around that I did not know how we were to get the better of that condition. [Her legs] are not beautiful now, but they are soft, free from swelling and pain and she walks as well as anyone. *I am never again going to think that anything is impossible".* The last sentence certainly deserves the added emphasis.

L-1. DO and DON'T. (2451, 4460, 4754). First, the DO: all through Chapter Seven, Spectro-Chrome in Diagnosed Disorders, Green, Lemon, and Turquoise are recommended to be tonated systemic front or back. They are tonated in this manner because what seems to be a localized condition may be more than it appears. Even if it is a local affair at that moment, those Colors can help prevent it from spreading and becoming an extensive problem. Further, Dinshah warned that some cases, even those of an obviously local nature (his editorial comment referred to a case of hearing loss), WILL NOT respond well until <u>systemic</u> tonations are utilized.

L-2. Second, the DON'T: It is safer for women not to tonate during their menses (periods) except for conditions directly involving the reproductive functions. At such times the aura is considerably altered; tonations then for other purposes may cause changes which, when the menses are over, leave the aura in an unbalanced state requiring further tonations.

M. FILTERS. (399, 764, 3146, 4348, 4857, OTYA208, SCME80). This complex topic is covered in depth in Chapter three, S-C Color Production.

N-1. ACCESSORIES (766, 797, 902, 947, 2478). Spectro-Chrome can be practiced adequately with amazingly little equipment or knowledge. The projector can be as simple as a bulb in a box, and there is the basic Color effect triad: Warm or stimulating, cool or sedating, and the those for circulation; the exceptions are those for the spleen, parathyroid, and pineal. On the other hand, Spectro-Chrome therapy can be implemented more conveniently with the help of a few unique accessories. Dinshah designed a number of devices to this end and some were marketed in small quantities, but have not been available for many years. They were accessories and not essential so the insignificant demand is understandable. The more important were:

N-2. Irradiator. It consisted of a little box placed inside the projector (or in Sunlight), holding five Color filters in front of five small water bottles. After a tonation, the water was drunk from the same bottle (or bottles) as the tonation Color. For a substitute method, see Chapter five, part two, paragraph O.

N-3. Itisometer. The Itisometer is described in paragraph F.

N-4. Sympathometer. It was a special clock running on a two-hour-fifty-six-minute cycle. Set it at Sunrise and through the day it indicated Forecast times and other information relating to the varying breath pressures; reset at Sunset for night Forecast times. Information from an Ephemeris was required for accuracy in setting it each day.

N-5. Kaspirameter. This device was to automatically count the heart and respiration rates and then calculate the ratio between them. To my knowledge no models were ever built; with present-day electronic equipment it should be relatively simple to construct a practical unit.

N-6. Antinude. This was a garment designed to be worn during tonations, with a closable flap over each area so unnecessary exposure could be avoided. It also was suitable for the Itisation procedure where temperature maintenance was of great consequence. Of course, many sizes would be needed as one size could not fit all; I remember my mother working on a sample.

N-7. Nurmand. The Graduate model Spectro-Chrome equipment (Color projector) was equipped with either a 1500- or 2000-watt bulb; it sold for $425. For those who believed more was better but were not so wealthy, in 1938 a less expensive 2000-watt projector, the Nurmand (meaning Brilliant) was unveiled at $250. As with the Graduate version, and as we would expect, there are no reports in the Spectro-Chrome magazines of its being more effective than the much less luminous projectors also available at that time.

N-8. Spirometer. Measuring the breath pressure from each nostril was made easier by using one of a set of calibrated rods. Each rod had a sensor (like a feather) on its end to indicate the extent of a nostril's pressure. The Spirometer determination was then checked against the Sympathometer indication for that time of day or night (N-4, above).

5. It is not unusual to take Light for granted, as though its only value is for vision. As learning progresses it will become apparent that Dinshah's view of Light was far ahead of his time and it will be better recognized that enabling sight is only one facet of the Power of Light.

* * * * *

CHAPTER FIVE

TECHNIQUE

1. It is your privilege to use this therapy in any manner you wish, but if the Spectro-Chrome system is to have a fair chance to produce the results expected of it, then its technique should be followed closely. Some of the details may not make much difference in all cases; still, the patient should be given every possible advantage. The more serious the condition, the more important it becomes to follow the recommendations.

2. The first part of this Chapter deals with important steps which would be prudent to put into practice before the need becomes urgent. For most people, the suggestions will require a considerable change in life style; each one can help toward better health. Part Two itemizes specifics for taking tonations.

PART ONE

a. The first line of health defense must be in the food we eat. It is well established that what we <u>don't</u> eat as well as what we do eat can hurt us. Lack of iodine may precipitate thyroid problems which can lead to diverse mental and physical inabilities; not enough vitamin C can result in abnormal bleeding tendencies, scurvy, etc.; shortage of vitamin D is related to rickets, convulsions, etc.; and recently, low zinc levels recently have been implicated in prostate ailments.

Non-animal sources to prevent all these conditions are readily found: iodine in sea kelp, vitamin C from peppers–citrus fruit–potatoes, vitamin D from Sunlight, zinc from wheat-germ (removed in white-flour processing). Decades ago Dinshah insisted that many diseases are essentially a state of chemical imbalance, so it is in your best interest to eat those foods which will maintain the best balance.

b. Eliminate from your diet: meat, poultry. fish, eggs, and all foods containing them.

c. Use whole-grain bread and flour, and brown rice; instead of white bread and flour, and white rice.

d. Minimize salt, refined sugar, and spices in the diet.

e. Avoid foods which are artificially colored or flavored, or contain chemical preservatives. You are better off without a micro-wave in your kitchen; virtually all of them leak radiation, especially as they age. How much they alter food cooked in them is open to debate.

f. Stop drinking coffee, tea, colas, and alcoholic beverages.

g. Use fresh foods in preference to frozen or canned. Eat raw foods in preference to cooked foods as their enzyme activity is retained. Cook only enough fresh food for prompt consumption because their etheric energies are soon dissipated. Frozen and canned foods were cooked in processing so have already lost their enzymes and etheric power.

h. All food should be thoroughly chewed. If this is burdensome with raw foods because of dental problems, a blender and juicer may be helpful. After eating, allow at least one hour before taking a tonation because digestion alters blood flow.

i. A vegetarian cookbook can help in putting the foregoing suggestions into practice. Vegetarianism has been rapidly growing in popularity and so has the number of suitable cookbooks, making the change from the typical diet much easier.

j. City water is invariably chemically treated, and often contains industrial contaminants. Fluorides are intentionally added to many municipal water supplies in Australia, England and the United States. Numerous countries have discontinued fluoridation, but their valid reasons for doing so are beyond the scope of this book (see Chapter 15, paragraph 2). It is much safer to drink and cook with distilled or spring water.

k. Stop use of tobacco, marijuana and other drugs, in any form. Avoid areas where their smoke is present.

l. Normal blood circulation is essential for effective tonations so it is advisable not to take a bath ½ hour before or after a tonation.

m. An old woodsman's saying goes, "When your feet are cold, put a cap on your head." The head receives approximately one- sixth of all blood circulation though the brain constitutes only perhaps one-fortieth of body weight (seven times more flow). With this veritable torrent of blood coursing through the head, it is prudent to give it at least as much protection against heat loss as the rest of the body. If the ambient temperature dictates clothes for your body then your head deserves the same consideration. This is particularly important when sick, so the body's vital resources will be conserved.

n. High-heeled shoes upset the natural balance of the spine, and may cause disorders of an obscure character (especially in women). Wear comfortable low-heeled shoes (or sandals, etc.), or go bare-foot when circumstances will permit it.

o. Ideally, sleep in a separate bed, especially when ill. The aura of one person is likely to interfere with that of another, to the detriment of one person or the other. Tonate in a separate bed.

p. Ideally, sleep and tonate with the head toward the North.

q. Bowel movements can be materially aided by squatting in the same posture used when the necessity arises in the woods. Being seated on a toilet hinders the anal sphincters from opening. The squatting posture decreases the internal pressure required to produce the movement and thereby lessens the likelihood of developing hemorrhoids or rectal prolapse. Moistening bathroom tissue with water avoids excessive friction on delicate tissues, and is certainly a more hygienic practice.

r. Enemas and laxatives should not be used except in emergencies. They will be unnecessary if a diet suitable for human digestion is consumed – with temporary help from Spectro-Chrome to energize the internal "machinery."

s. Exercise is important for maintaining blood circulation and essential for lymphatic circulation. Even when a person is bedfast, it is rarely an excuse to do nothing at all; every little bit helps. Of course, discretion must be used in all cases to prevent overtaxing.

t. Avoid exposure to fluorescent lighting whenever possible. All fluorescent tubes emit powerful energies in some parts of the spectrum (Fraunhofer Lines) due to the method they use to produce Light. Besides these emission "peaks", some so-called "full-spectrum" fluorescent lamps have many frequencies missing – a combination of emission and omission errors. Long-term exposure to these energy aberrations may, sooner or later, cause health problems. Typical household incandescent bulbs are not perfect as a Light source but they <u>do not</u> radiate sharp peaks of energy and <u>do</u> have a complete visible spectrum. This does not apply to incandescent bulbs made with Neodymium (**Chromalux, Bulbrite**, etc.) which are promoted as "full spectrum" but admit to having virtually NO Yellow Light – keep them out of your home. These important technicalities are demonstrated visually with a spectroscope in our video **My Spectro-Chrome**, and on the inside front cover of this book.

u. If sunglasses must be worn, use a neutral tint (gray). Using color-shaded prescription glasses is somewhat similar to taking a continuous tonation.

v. Check the instructions before hanging pest-destroying strips. Some warn against using them in rooms occupied by infants or elderly persons. If it is not safe for them, why should anyone risk using them?

PART TWO
HOW TO TAKE A TONATION

A. Select a tonation time from the Variant Breath Forecast. If your locality requires an adjustment to the times given in the Forecast, consult the table sent with your Forecast and make the appropriate correction. When feasible, tonate infra-Green Colors at daylight Forecast times; ultra-Green tonations at night are generally preferred as they tend to be relaxing.

B. The room should be warm enough to prevent chilling the person taking the tonation; for systemic tonations the room should be quite warm. A portable electric heater can be used in the tonation room to avoid over-heating the rest of the house. If the heater emits appreciable Light, do not allow it to shine toward the person being tonated.

C. Face the South if seated during a tonation. If lying down, have the top of the head toward the North – toward the East if unavoidable. Tonating while lying down is preferred; sitting for an hour is somewhat stressful.

D. For tonating front areas, lie on the back or either side. For tonating back areas, lie on either side but not on the abdomen. Lying on the abdomen reverses the body's electrical polarity in relation to the Earth.

E. Darken the tonation room as much as practical; total darkness is not required.

F. Remove the clothing necessary to expose the areas to be tonated; it is essential for tonations to be on bare skin.

G. Insert filters in the projector for the Color selected. Turn on the projector at the Forecast time. Aim the beam at appropriate area/s; if it is for a systemic tonation from the bottoms of the feet, move the projector to the bottom of the bed and aim it from the feet all the way up to the head. Each tonation is normally <u>one Color for one hour</u>. If two or more Colors are to be tonated, do so at separate Forecast times.

H. One tonation in the day and one at night is generally sufficient, and gives the body time to equilibrate itself between tonations. Nature can be helped but not rushed.

I. In some severe acute conditions (burns, poison ivy, headache, sprains, etc.) a continuous tonation may be employed. If an infant is given an extended tonation, cover the eyes at night to preserve the diurnal/nocturnal cycle.

J. The darker Colors such as Magenta may be difficult to adjust on the person, especially when a large area coverage (systemic) is required. If this problem is encountered, do this: Turn on the projector with a light-colored filter in it, place it so the beam covers the desired areas, then replace the filter with those needed for the tonation.

K. Do not be concerned if the darker Colors cannot easily be seen on the body. The effect is what matters and this takes place on the (generally) invisible aura whether you can see the Color well or not. The quality of the Color is far more important than the quantity.

L. Spectro-Chrome can work through the aura whether you are awake or asleep, conscious or unconscious, but its power can be augmented or hindered by your mental state. Do not try to read, watch TV, or listen to a radio while tonating. Reinforce the tonation with mental energy. Also, it is advisable to rest in the darkened room for a few minutes after a tonation.

M. Allow at least an hour between eating and tonating. An exception may be made if the tonation is to aid digestion, and the tonation may be shorter than the standard one hour to lessen the likelihood of throwing-up.

N. Women should not take tonations during their menstrual periods except for excessive flow or pain, or in emergencies (see Chapter four, para. L-2).

O. If Color-charged water is desired to augment the tonation, it can be made by placing a clear glass of water on a chair near the person taking the tonation (but not within 18-inches) so the Color also shines on the water glass. The patient drinks the water at the end of the tonation. Women have altered auras during their menstrual periods so should avoid handling Color-charged water (or cooking for that matter) except for their own use.

P. Color-charged water is not expected to be so effective as a tonation but when taking a tonation is not convenient it can be used as a substitute. Water can be easily Color-charged: Remove the top from a cardboard box and place a bottle (colorless) of water in the box. Cover the box opening with a filter of the desired Color. Place the assembled box/bottle/filter near a Light source or sunny window; allow to charge at least an hour. Drink the water about 45 minutes after the beginning of a Forecast time.

Q. Serious activities should be avoided during eclipses; do not eat, sleep, study, take tonations, etc. The Forecast lists eclipse dates and times.

R. When time is not of the essence, begin a program of tonations as outlined in the following paragraphs – 1 through 9, then continue with Colors for the specific condition. If there is some urgency, begin in the same manner and also start tonations for the condition. Emergency cases of course must be treated immediately with appropriate measures.

1. Begin tonations with Green systemic front. Follow with Turquoise systemic front for recent (acute) conditions, or Lemon systemic front for persistent (chronic) conditions. Many illnesses cause changes in circulation so Magenta on areas #4-5-18 is usually beneficial.

2. The ratio of heart rate/respiration is normally between 4-to-1 and 5-to-1; a ratio in this range indicates a hopeful case. A ratio of 3-to-1 signals a doubtful case and a reason for greater vigilance. If the ratio nears 2-to-1, death may be near.

3. The average adult male heart rate is about 72 to 80 beats per minute, with most females somewhat higher. Children have considerably higher rates while athletes generally have much lower rates, but in any case the ratio should be between 4-to-1 and 5-to-1. Magenta tonations on areas #4-5-18 often can be used as a test. If Magenta raises the heart rate then Scarlet may be used on the same areas as it is a stimulant, or if the heart rate slows then Purple may be used as it is a depressant; in either event conclude with a few Magenta tonations.

4. For feeble pulse or low heart rate, tonate Scarlet on areas #4-5-18 or systemic front and back in severe or stubborn cases. For a hard pulse or high heart rate, tonate Purple on areas #4-5-18 or systemic front and back in severe or stubborn cases. In some cases or an emergency situation, tonations may be more effective when given systemic from the bottoms of the feet, and/or with two projectors–simultaneously front and back (see Chapter four, paragraph H). For erratic heart beat (cardiac arrhythmia), see Color schedule #71 in Chapter seven.

5. If neither Purple or Scarlet is indicated, tonate a few Magenta on areas #4-5-18.

6. For shallow respiration or rate, tonate Orange on Areas #3-4-5-17. For high respiration rate, tonate Indigo on areas #3-4-5-17.

7. Due consideration must be given to digestive and eliminative functions. Unless contra-indicated, a few tonations of Yellow on areas #6-7-8-9-10 should be taken to tone-up those systems. Use infra-Green Colors on those areas to increase activity or ultra-green Colors to decrease activity.

8. If urine is scanty, tonate Scarlet on areas # 4-5-18 (or only #18 if blood pressure is high); an increase in fluid intake may be necessary. If urine is excessive, tonate Purple on areas #4-5-18; a decrease in fluid may be required (diabetes or other disorder may be present and require attention).

9. It is possible in some cases to need both Purple and Scarlet (of course, in separate tonations). For instance, a high fever with urine suppression–tonate Blue systemic front, Purple on areas #4-5 and Scarlet on area #18 (at separate tonations). When the crisis has passed, the fever drops and urination nears normal, tonate Magenta on #4-5-18.

S. The aura normally will accept only enough of any Color to maintain its Color balance. However, in sickness the aura does not have so great a power of selectivity. The more serious the case, the more important it becomes to use care in the selection of tonation Colors, and follow the recommended Spectro-Chrome technique.

T. It is not necessary to use any particular sequence when tonating more than one color (at separate Forecast times) but paragraph A (above) suggests a day infra-Green and night ultra-Green arrangement when practical. When awake and taking a tonation, the eyes should be open and looking toward the Color source but not necessarily directly at it.

U. When using more than one Color for a condition, one Color might be used once followed by another Color twice or more (depending on the expected or perceived effect of each Color) and so on. However, until a thorough knowledge of the attributes of each Color has been acquired, it may be prudent to simply use the Colors in rotation.

V. Due to their cleansing action, it is not uncommon for a rash to appear or diarrhea to occur when beginning tonations of Lemon, Green, or Turquoise. Continue with the tonations and when the "debris" inside has been eliminated then the rash or diarrhea will disappear.

W. If all the Colors being tonated are on one side of the spectrum, occasionally try a Color on the other side of the spectrum. For instance, if Blue has been used for some days and a fever will not go any lower, tonate Yellow systemic and then return to Blue. Another option is to try a "stronger" Blue (such as Indigo) which has greater cooling energy though less for cleansing. Because of differences in individual cases, Color suggestions are not immutable – they are guidelines and judgement is often a requisite.

X. The usual tonations for convalescence are Lemon systemic (chronic alterative), followed by Yellow (lymphatic system stimulant). Magenta (circulatory system builder) systemic is used with the Lemon and Yellow if there had been a hemorrhage. Conclude with Turquoise systemic.

Y. When to all outward appearances health has been restored, after an acute case take a few Turquoise systemic tonations, or Lemon systemic if a chronic case. This is not needed if these were the main Colors in the respective cases. However, if tonations were taken for more than two weeks, see paragraph X above.

Z. Yes, there is much to learn here, and you will benefit by observing these suggestions which have evolved from decades of experience with the Spectro-Chrome System.

*   *   *   *   *

CHAPTER SIX

SPECTRO-CHROME COLOR ATTRIBUTES
and
TONATIONS by SYMPTOMS

1. Many disorders can be tonated by their symptoms. It is important to put into practice the instructions and technique in Chapter five. Another requisite is an understanding of the major attributes of each Color. These are listed in the following table with their equivalent medical terms in parentheses.

2. An "attribute" is an effect expected to be generated within the body when that Color is tonated *if* the Color energy is needed *and* it is within the constitutional abilities of the person to utilize it. Results may be achieved in one tonation or a week or a month or more; it may be amazingly rapid or distressingly slow, but is usually somewhere in-between.

3. Keep in mind that besides its own attributes, each Color also produces (with less efficacy) the effects of the Color before it in the spectrum as well as the Color after it. Two examples: Orange also gives (in some measure) the effects of Red and Yellow; and Blue gives (in some measure) the effects of Turquoise and Indigo (technically, the influence goes somewhat further). These either-side essences are in some cases quite useful and even surprising, in other cases a specific Color may be essential to attain the desired result.

4. This book has many details to be remembered and if it is to be truly educational this is unavoidable. So, here is one more important detail. In this and the following Chapter you will see many caged, bold-faced numbers like this: ‖00‖. These caged numbers always will be directly after the name of a Color, for instance: Turquoise ‖00‖. *Do not* confuse them with the numbers used to identify tonation areas which are printed in regular figures—#4-5-18. Once again, the caged, bold-faced numbers refer to the attribute or reason for tonating that particular Color, and any like these—#6-7-8—identify the areas on which the Color is to be tonated. The foregoing details are an essential link between this Chapter and the Color schedules in the following Chapter.

ATTRIBUTES OF SPECTRO-CHROME COLORS

Attri- bute #	S-C Color:	Attribute:
	RED	

‖1‖ Stimulates the sensory nervous system which energizes the senses: sight, hearing, touch, taste, and smell.

‖2‖ Liver builder and stimulant, areas #7-8.

‖3‖ Builds platelets, hemoglobin, etc., of the blood (hemoglobic).

‖4‖ Causes rapid expulsion of debris through the skin; may induce skin redness, itching, pimples, until the internal cleansing process is completed (irritant, pustulant).

‖5‖ Counter-agent for burns from x-rays, ultra-violet, etc.

ORANGE

||6|| Lung builder, and respiratory stimulant, areas #3-4-5-17.

||7|| Thyroid builder and stimulant, area #3.

||8|| Parathyroid depressant, area #3.

||9|| Relieves cramps and muscle spasms (antispasmodic).

||10|| Stimulates mammary glands to increase milk production, areas 4-5 (galactagogue).

||11|| Stomach stimulant, areas #6-8 (stomachic).

||12|| Assists vomiting when stomach contains unsuitable matter, areas #6-8 (emetic).

||13|| Relieves flatulence or gas in the digestive tract, areas #6-7-8-9-10-18-19 (carminative).

||14|| Bone builder; corrects bone softness, rickets, by calcium effect.

||15|| Tissue stimulant, decongestant.

YELLOW

||16|| Stimulates the motor nervous system which energizes the muscles. Nerve builder for sensory and motor systems.

||17|| Stimulates the lymphatic system. Mild tissue stimulant.

||18|| Stimulates the intestines, pancreas, and production of digestive fluids – bile, hydrochloric acid, etc., areas #6-7-8-9-10-18-19 (digestant, cholagogue).

||19|| Increases bowel movements, areas #9-10-18-19 (cathartic).

||20|| Spleen depressant; equilibrator in melancholia, balances areas #6-7 through the portal circulation.

||21|| Expels worms and parasites (anthelmintic).

LEMON

||22|| Produces a favorable change in the processes of nutrition and repair in persistent disorders (chronic alterative). Dissolves blood clots.

||23|| Promotes coughing to expel mucus and fluids from the lungs and air passages, areas #2-3-4-5-17 (expectorant).

||24|| Bone builder, by phosphorus effect.

||25|| Brain stimulant, areas #1-15.

||26|| Thymus builder and stimulant, areas #4-5.

||27|| Mildly stimulates digestive system, areas #6-7-8-9-10-18-19 (laxative).

||28|| Equilibrator after extended use of ultra-Green tonations.

GREEN

||29|| Cerebral equilibrator, areas #1-15. Physical equilibrator, systemic front.

||30|| Pituitary stimulant and equilibrator, area #1

||31|| Stimulates the rebuilding of muscles and tissues.

||32|| Destroys micro-organisms, germs, bacteria; cleanses and prevents decay (germicide, bactericide, disinfectant, antiseptic).

TURQUOISE

‖33‖ Produces a favorable change in the processes of nutrition and repair in recent disorders (acute alterative).

‖34‖ Brain depressant, areas #1-15.

‖35‖ Skin tonic. Rebuilds burned skin (antipyrotic).

‖36‖ Equilibrator after extended use of infra-Green tonations.

BLUE

‖37‖ Relieves itching, and irritation of abraded surfaces (antipruritic, demulcent).

‖38‖ Encourages perspiration (diaphoretic).

‖39‖ Mild sedative. Reduces or removes fever and inflammation (febrifuge, antipyretic, antiphlogistic).

‖40‖ Pineal stimulant Area #1; builds vitality.

INDIGO

‖41‖ Parathyroid builder and stimulant, area #3.

‖42‖ Thyroid depressant, area #3.

‖43‖ Respiratory depressant, areas #3-4-5-17.

‖44‖ Causes contraction, controls abscesses, lessens secretions, arrests discharges and hemorrhages (astringent, antipyic, anti-emetic, hemostatic).

‖45‖ Promotes the production of phagocytes which destroy harmful micro-organisms, bacteria, germs, etc.

‖46‖ Mammary depressant reduces milk production, areas #4-5 (lactifuge).

‖47‖ Eases suffering, lessens excitement and over-activity (sedative).

VIOLET

‖48‖ Spleen builder and stimulant, area #6.

‖49‖ Decreases muscular activity, including the heart muscles.

‖50‖ Lymphatic glands depressant, systemic front. Pancreas depressant, areas #8-18.

‖51‖ Decreases activity of the nervous systems (tranquilizer).

‖52‖ Promotes production of leucocytes, white (Violet) blood cells.

PURPLE

‖53‖ Kidney and adrenal depressant, area #18.

‖54‖ Decreases sensitivity to pain. Induces relaxation and sleep (soporific).

‖55‖ Increases functional activity of the veins.

‖56‖ Lowers blood pressure by three effects:

    ‖57‖ Dilates blood vessels (vasodilator)

    ‖58‖ Reduces the heart rate, areas #4-5

    ‖59‖ Decreases activity of the kidneys and adrenals, area #18; and the chromaffin system, systemic front and back.

‖60‖ Lowers body temperature.

‖61‖ Controls fever and high blood pressure in malaria and recurrent fevers (antimalarial).

‖62‖ Emotional and reproductive system depressant. Builds sex powers by decreasing sensitivity and desire when excessive (anaphrodisiac).

‖63‖ Moderates blood pressure between heart and lungs, areas #4-5. Controls lung hemorrhages; some cases may respond better to Magenta or Scarlet (use heart/respiration ratio as a guide, see Chapter five, Technique). When in doubt try Purple first. The foregoing approach also applies to cases of dry coughing (non-productive of phlegm).

MAGENTA

‖64‖ Emotional equilibrator, and auric builder, systemic front.
Builds and equilibrates the functional activity of:

   ‖65‖ Heart, areas #4-5 (cardiotonic)

   ‖66‖ Blood circulatory system

   ‖67‖ Kidneys and adrenals, area #18; and
       the chromaffin system, systemic front and back.

   ‖68‖ Reproductive system, areas #10-11

   ‖69‖ Kidneys, area #18.

SCARLET

‖70‖ Kidney and adrenal stimulant, area #18.

‖71‖ General stimulant. Increases functional activity of the arteries.

‖72‖ Raises blood pressure by three effects:

   ‖73‖ Constricts the blood vessels (vasoconstrictor)

   ‖74‖ Increases heart rate, areas #4-5

   ‖75‖ Stimulates activity of the kidneys and adrenals, area #18; and
       the chromaffin system, systemic front and back.

‖76‖ Accelerates fetal expulsion at time of delivery (ecbolic).

‖77‖ Emotional stimulant. Builds sex powers by increasing sensitivity and desire when deficient (aphrodisiac).

‖78‖ Stimulates the reproductive system, and menstrual function (emmenagogue).

5. The foregoing Table of Attributes lists the effects expected from each Spectro-Chrome Color when tonated on a live person. However, if an organ is missing from birth, completely removed or necrosed, it is then unreasonable to anticipate a favorable reaction from that particular area. On the other hand, if even a small part of an organ remains, it may be able to be regenerated or energized to the point where it is able to function adequately. Tonate Lemon systemic ‖22‖ (chronic alterative) and the appropriate Color stimulant or builder for the organ involved. Many disorders can be tonated in this manner, beginning of course with the instructions in Chapter five, Technique.

6. Perseverance in tonating is often essential, especially if the case is long-standing. It will be well worth the effort because every organ has specific functions to perform and when any area falters or fails, detrimental repercussions eventually must arise somewhere in the body.

7. The basic tonations for obvious conditions such as burns, cuts, colds, nose-bleed, sprains, insomnia, loose teeth, indigestion, abortion, sterility, etc., are found in the next Chapter, Spectro-Chrome in Diagnosed Disorders. Much can be learned by studying how these and other conditions are tonated because in the next Chapter every Color schedule tells you why each Color in it is recommended. It does so by using the now familiar caged, bold-faced numbers: ‖**00**‖. The knowledge gained will show some interesting patterns. Explained here is the "what and why" of four of these patterns.

8-A. The first pattern shows:

For all disorders, except a few emergency conditions, Green or one of its derivatives (Lemon, Turquoise) is included in the tonation program.

This is why:

8-B. Green as physical equilibrator (attribute ‖**29**‖) tends to bring all bodily functions to their normal levels. In recent (acute) disorders there is usually a rise in body temperature, at least at the focus of the problem. Turquoise (½ Green, ½ Blue) is the acute alterative (attribute ‖**33**‖) because it has some of the governing and cleansing power needed due to its Green component and has some fever controlling ability from its Blue component. For those reasons tonate Turquoise systemic in recent disorders with little or moderate fever. Tonate Green and Blue individually if the fever rises, and add Purple (attribute ‖**60**‖) on areas #4-5 whenever a high fever exists.

8-C. When a feeling of "coming down with something" is noticed, tonate once with Magenta or Scarlet on areas #1-2-3-4-5, and at later Forecast times with Turquoise systemic. Valuable time should not be wasted waiting to see what develops or for a "differential diagnosis". Chapter five, Technique, paragraph R, has more information for beginning tonations under differing circumstances.

8-D. In persistent disorders the reparative and recuperative powers may have waned. Lemon (½ Green, ½ Yellow) is the chronic alterative (attribute ‖**22**‖) because it has some of the governing and cleansing power needed due to its Green component and has some stimulating ability from its Yellow component. Use Lemon ‖**22**‖ in all persistent disorders; if fever recurs tonate an ultra-Green Color as suggested in paragraph 8-B until there is little or no fever, then revert to Lemon and any other Colors which were being tonated.

9-A. The second pattern shows:

The invariable use of Purple, Magenta, and/or Scarlet in all disorders involving the heart, blood circulation, or reproductive system; and when beginning tonations. This is why:

9-B. Chapter five, Technique, recommends when beginning tonations to include one or more of those Colors because all repairs to the body can be accomplished only by one medium and that is through the blood circulation. After initial use of these Colors, usually it will be discretional whether to continue tonating any of them. However, it is prudent to tonate an occasional Magenta ‖**65**‖ on areas #4-5 if a series of tonations continues for more than a week or two.

9-C. The emotions and blood circulation are markedly involved in the adequate functioning of the reproductive system. The three Colors of this pattern are indispensable in cases of reproductive dysfunction. Study the Color schedules in

Chapter seven, Diagnosed Disorders, noting the Colors recommended and their attributes for problems of this nature.

10-A. The third pattern shows:

Color schedules #275, 276, are used for long-term tonations in cases of paralysis, sensory deficit or loss, or nerve damage.

This is why:

10 B. Lemon ‖22‖ is used in all persistent disorders; paralysis is very likely to be persistent in nature. Yellow, Orange (and Red in sensory cases) are also listed because Yellow ‖16‖ is the nerve builder, Orange is ½ Yellow and ½ Red so it has some properties for energizing both motor and sensory nerves, and Red ‖1‖ is the strongest sensory stimulant. Note that the tonations gradually work through the infra-side of the spectrum, increasing at each step. As it is not prudent to start an automobile in high gear, similarly it is most effective to tonate through the range of Spectro-Chrome "gears" in these cases.

11-A. The fourth pattern shows:

Indigo tonations in disorders involving one or more of these: Bleeding, abscesses, effusion, suppuration, pain.

This is why:

11-B. Indigo works in these disorders with a three-way effort. First: (Attribute ‖44‖) – by contracting tissues, bleeding and effusions are controlled; the astringent effect also contains and limits the spread of abscesses. Second: (Attribute ‖45‖) – by promoting the production of phagocytes, the extent of infection from a wound or abscess is lessened, thereby accelerating the healing process. Third: (Attribute ‖47‖) – the pain in any of these circumstances is minimized.

12. These examples illustrate the reasoning for part of the Spectro-Chrome system. For an in-depth understanding of the logic for each Color attribute, read the **Spectro-Chrome Metry Encyclopedia.**

13. It should be realized that while we can use symptoms as a guide for tonating, it is the underlying cause we expect to change. When the cause has been removed the symptoms will vanish. Further, as each Color has several attributes it is possible to be tonating a disorder and at the same time be arresting another condition which has not yet developed to the point of exhibiting symptoms (subclinical). This marvelous ability of Spectro-Chrome to do more than is asked of it is due in part to the capability of each Color to generate a fraction of the effects of the Colors on either side of it.

14. Spectro-Chrome is not an instant cure-all and has limitations as do all therapies, but it should make life more pleasant for most people until Gabriel blows his horn.

* * * * *

CHAPTER SEVEN

SPECTRO-CHROME in DIAGNOSED DISORDERS

1. When a diagnosis has been made with certainty, by any method, this Chapter can be of service. It lists Colors to tonate for disorders according to their common names, and medical names. Obvious conditions (burns, cuts, colds, nosebleed, etc.) which usually do not require a diagnosis are also included.

2. Much of the material in the following paragraphs is also found in preceding Chapters. It is repeated here because all too many readers do not take the time to study the complete technique, apparently thinking that the Color schedule for their particular problem is all the information they need. Those who do so are certainly short-changing themselves and Spectro-Chrome by not taking advantage of the knowledge gained in more than seven decades of use. You paid for the whole book, why not learn all you can from it?

3. It must be understood that the Colors listed in each schedule are for typical or "classic" case symptoms. They should not be regarded as the only Colors required in every case because there can be variations and complications. To help in determining whether the Colors given in a Color schedule are those needed in a specific case, use the Color attribute numbers – ‖00‖. If any of the attributes do not agree with the symptoms of the case at hand, additional or substitutional Colors may be selected from the Table of Attributes (Chapter six). If complications constitute a distinct and identifiable disorder, the Colors from its schedule may be added.

4. Most of the Color schedules for acute disorders recommend Turquoise ‖33‖ because it is a combination of, at least partly, the effects of both Green and Blue. However, in some cases it may be necessary to tonate Green and Blue in separate tonations (at Forecast times when possible) even if there is only a little fever, to attain the desired result. From the **Spectro-Chrome Metry Encyclopedia** it will be learned that all disorders with the medical suffix "itis" (inflammation) can be tonated primarily with Blue, and other Colors as circumstances dictate. A significant advantage with Spectro-Chrome is that it does not act in the same manner as conventional medicine or drugs (or even relatively natural materials such as herbs or teas) in that it will not "force" an issue; when the body has made the physiologic changes necessary for its well-being, the fever or other symptoms will abate.

5. When a Color schedule lists two or more Colors, use them in rotation (at separate Forecast times) until sufficient skill has been attained in judging the effect of each Color (Chapter five, paragraphs T, U). In cases of short duration such as uncomplicated measles, convalescence may require only two or three tonations of each Color. After an extended series of tonations for a long-standing or refractory disorder, convalescence may require a Color for many days before proceeding to the next Color. Just how long each Color should be tonated depends in part on how long the condition existed and in part how the person reacts.

6. In this Chapter, the areas to be tonated are listed without the word "area". For example, when you are to tonate Green on areas #1 and #15 it will read:

"Green on #1-15". Once again: This style of numbers tells the reason or reasons (attribute/s) for using a Color—‖**00**‖, and these tell on which areas to tonate it: #0-0-00. A reminder of these numbering styles is reproduced at the bottom of each odd-numbered page.

7. Lemon, Green, and Turquoise are usually given as systemic tonations even when the disorder appears to be a local affair. This is to make full use of their attributes as well as to limit the spreading of the condition. Furthermore, some seemingly local ailments WILL NOT respond properly until systemic tonations are used (see Chapter four, paragraph L-1).

8. A word of caution is in order here. If Spectro-Chrome is used in conjunction with other healing methods, it would be well to give some thought to possible interactions (synergism). The nature and extent of their combined effects may be difficult to predict. An example:

A man has been taking a drug orally for an intestinal complaint. He now begins a series of Yellow tonations on his abdomen while continuing with the medication. Some conceivable effects from the Spectro-Chrome/drug combination could be:

1. An <u>increase</u> in drug absorption due to greater lacteal activity (Yellow ‖**17**‖, lymphatic system stimulant), or

2. A <u>decrease</u> in drug absorption due to more rapid passage of material through the intestinal tract (Yellow ‖**18**‖, digestive stimulant), or

3. No change in drug assimilation due to a balance between the other two possible effects.

For reasons such as these, Dinshah advised using only ONE HEALING METHOD AT A TIME, with an exception for emergency situations. It is of course each person's responsibility how to proceed, or watch for interactions.

Index of Spectro-Chrome Color Schedules

309	Anemia, sickle cell	47	Bronchitis, acute
69a	Aneurism, aortic	48	Bronchitis, chronic or fibrinous
69b	Aneurism, multiple arterial	239	Brucellosis
2	Aneurism, cerebral	303	Bruises
51	Angina Ludovici	238	Bubonic plague
74	Angina pectoris	172	Buerger's disease
293	Anorexia nervosa	189	Burns, infra-red (heat)
1	Anosmia	190	Burns, ultra-violet (cold)
194	Anoxemia	209	Bursitis, acute
256	Anterior poliomyelitis	210	Bursitis, chronic
246	Anthrax	195	Caisson disease
147	Anuria	324	Candida
69a	Aortic aneurism	177	Cancer
133	Apathy, sexual	241	Canker sores
1	Aphasia	185	Carbuncle
1	Aphemia	177	Carcinoma
241	Aphthous stomatitis	67	Cardiac: insufficiency – dilatation – hypertrophy – incompetence – regurgitation
108	Appendicitis		
1	Apraxia		
71	Arrhythmia, cardiac	71	Cardiac arrhythmia
171	Arteriosclerosis	68	Cardiac valvular stenosis
203	Arsenic poisoning	65	Carditis, acute
212	Arthritis	66	Carditis, chronic
81	Asbestos	326	Carpal tunnel syndrome
115	Ascites	280	Carrier
205	Asphyxial sunstroke	298	Cat-scratch disease
78	Asthma	14	Cataract
58	Ateliosis	107	Catarrhal enteritis
302	Athletic heart syndrome	2	Cerebral abscess or aneurism
297	Bacteremia	5	Cerebral concussion
24	Bad breath	2	Cerebral embolism or hemorrhage
124	Banti's disease	253	Cerebral tabes
195	Bends	2	Cerebral thrombosis
298	Benign lymphoreticulosis	3	Cerebral tumor
177	Benign tumors	233	Cerebrospinal fever
180	Beri-beri	292	Cerebrovascular hemorrhagic accident (stroke)
303	Black-eye		
81	Blacklung	127	Chancre
188	Bleeding injury	225	Chickenpox
282	Blood clots	284	Chills
277	Blood pressure, high	45	Child-crowing
197	Blood pressure, loss of	175	Chlorosis
278	Blood pressure, low	13	Choked disk
185	Boils	98	Cholelithiasis
208	Bone fractures	236	Cholera asiatica
73	Bradycardia	104	Cholera infantum
	Brain, see "cerebral"	236	Cholera nostras
234	Breakbone fever	263	Chorea, acute
77	Bronchiectasis	159	Chromaffin system insufficiency

312	Cigarette smoking
97b	Cirrhosis, liver
29	Cold
112	Colitis
301	Congenital adrenal hyperplasia
109	Constipation
265	Convulsions, infantile
29	Coryza, acute
30	Coryza, chronic
109	Costiveness
306	Cough, non-productive
305	Cough, productive
196	Cramps, muscle
60	Cretinism
162	Cushing's syndrome
188	Cuts
288	Cystic fibrosis
156	Cystinuria
151	Cystitis
177	Cysts
1	Deafness
256	Degenerative myelitis
200	Delirium tremens
234	Dengue
184	Dercum's disease
191	Dermatitis
122	Diabetes insipidus
120	Diabetes mellitus
107	Diarrhea
256	Diffuse sclerosis
325	Digestive hyperacidity
232	Diphtheria
314	Discharges
195	Diver's paralysis
307	Diverticulosis
11	Dizziness, information on
286	Dropsy
268	Drowsiness, chronic
201	Drug addiction
306	Dry cough – non-productive
326	Dry-eye syndrome
26	Dry mouth
58	Dwarfism
1	Dyslexia
112	Dysentery
317	Earache
186	Eczema
286	Edema
105	Emesis

323	Emotional disorders
7	Emotional stress
81	Emphysema
87	Empyema of the chest
2	Encephalitis
308	Endometriosis
110	Enteroptosis
243	Ephemeral fever
241	Epidemic stomatitis
266	Epilepsy
32	Epistaxis
55	Esophageal cancer
250	Erysipelas
169	Erythromelalgia
54	Esophagismus
52	Esophagitis, acute
53	Esophagitis, chronic
25	Excess saliva
21	Exodontia
61	Exophthalmic goiter
21	Extraction, tooth
9	Facial hemiatrophy
6	Falling hair
131	Falling womb
222	Farcy
313	Farsightedness
70	Fatty heart
95	Fatty liver
243	Febricula
24	Fetor oris
315	Fever. Also, see under specific headings
111	Filariasis
106	Flatulence
231	Flu
204	Food poisoning
54	Foodpipe spasm
270	Functional overactivity
315	FUO (fever, unexplained origin)
185	Furuncle
98	Gallstones
282	Gangrene
100	Gastritis, acute
101	Gastritis, chronic
112	Gastroenteritis, acute
322	Genital herpes
253	General paresis
17	Geographical tongue
19	Gingivitis
222	Glanders

245	Glandular fever
15	Glaucoma
121	Glycosuria (glucose in urine)
61	Goiter, exophthalmic
59	Goiter, simple
125	Gonorrhea
182	Gout
61	Graves' disease
231	Grippe
19	Gum disease
264	Habit spasms or tics
171	Hardening of the arteries
271	Hatred
31	Hay fever
7	Headache, nervous
8	Headache, migraine
206	Heat prostration
	Heart, see "cardiac"
103	Hematemesis
167	Hematomyelia
16	Hematorachis
148	Hematuria
150	Hemoglobinuria
267	Hemophilia
80	Hemoptysis
188	Hemorrhage
164	Hemorrhoids
97a	Hepatitis, acute
97b	Hepatitis, chronic
211	Hernia
287	Herniated nucleus pulposus
322	Herpes, genital or simplex
254	Herpes zoster
49	Hiccup
277	High blood pressure
178	Hodgkin's disease
111	Hookworms
271	Human repugnance
4	Hydrocephalus
157	Hydronephrosis
247	Hydrophobia
88	Hydrothorax
325	Hyperacidity, digestive
313	Hyperopia
119	Hyperinsulinism, chronic
269	Hyperkinesis
64	Hyperparathyroidism
277	Hypertension
61	Hyperthyroidism
215	Hypertrophic pulmonary-

	osteo-arthropathy
119	Hypoglycemia
63	Hypoparathyroidism
278	Hypotension
60	Hypothyroidism
273	Hysteria
93	Icterus
99	Icterus gravis
289	Immune deficiency
133	Impotence
319	Incontinence, urinary
155	Indicanuria
106	Indigestion
265	Infantile convulsions
256	Infantile hemiplegia
58	Infantilism
245	Infectious mononucleosis
304	Inflammation
231	Influenza
191	Insect bites
7	Insomnia
282	Intermittent claudication
111	Intestinal parasites
93	Jaundice
	Kidney – also see "renal" and "nephritis"
158	Kidney stones
11	Labyrinthine vertigo
42	Laryngitis, acute
43	Laryngitis, chronic
44	Laryngitis, edematous
45	Laryngitis, spasmodic
46	Laryngitis, tuberculous
202	Lead poisoning
242	Leprosy
176	Leukemia
18	Leukoplakia buccalis
128	Leukorrhea
153	Lithuria
255	Little's disease
94	Liver cancer
97b	Liver cirrhosis
214	Lobstein's disease
321	Localized scratch dermatitis
248	Lockjaw
252	Locomotor ataxia
23	Loose teeth
278	Low blood pressure
119	Low blood sugar

50	Pharyngeal ulceration	247	Rabies
38	Pharyngitis, acute	190	Radiation burns
39	Pharyngitis, chronic	72	Rapid heart
277	Pheochromocytoma	169	Red neuralgia
172	Phlebitis	226	Relapsing fever
323	Phobias	146	Renal sclerosis
164	Piles	300	Retinitis pigmentosa
294	Pinworms	327	Retinopathy
85	Pleurisy, acute	173	Reynaud's disease
86	Pleurisy, chronic	235	Rheumatic fever
87	Pleurisy, purulent	212	Rheumatoid arthritis
152	Pneumaturia	181	Rickets
81	Pneumoconiosis	233	Rocky Mountain fever
76	Pneumonia	111	Round worms
182	Podagra	225	Rubella
203	Poisoning, arsenic	211	Rupture, reducible
204	Poisoning, food	28	Salivary gland inflammation
202	Poisoning, lead	177	Sarcoma
256	Polio	229	Scarlet fever
141	Post-pregnancy: increasing milk production	323	Schizophrenia
		217	Sciatica
140	Pregnancy: excessive flow after delivery	193	Scleroderma
		75	Scrofula
139	Pregnancy: long labor	179	Scurvy
136	Pregnancy: miscarriage impending	163	Secondary adrenal insufficiency
		311	Secondary lymphedema
137	Pregnancy, normal	299	Senile dementia
139	Pregnancy: slow placental separation	275	Sensory nervous system schedule
		249	Septicemia
135	Pregnancy, vomiting in	238	Septicemic plague
139	Pregnancy: weak contractions	251	Septicopyemia
147	Prerenal anuria	134	Sex craving
320	Preventive tonations	133	Sexual: apathy – impotence– sterility
256	Primary lymphadema		
305	Productive cough	262	Shaking palsy
256	Progressive bulbar paralysis	254	Shingles
320	Prophylaxis	284	Shivering
142	Prostate enlargement	197	Shock
143	Prostate inflammation, acute	309	Sickle cell anemia
144	Prostate inflammation, chronic	81	Silicosis
186	Psoriasis (skin disorder)	49	Singultus
221	Psorospermiasis	295	Sinusitis, sinus inflammation
25	Ptyalism	186	Skin diseases
84	Pulmonary carcinoma	187	Skin hemorrhages
75	Pulmonary fibrosis or phthisis	219	Sleeping sickness
187	Purpura	287	Slipped spinal disk
251	Pyemia	73	Slow heart
15	Pyelitis and pyuria	227	Smallpox
36	Quinsy	37	Smoker's throat

9. The index on the previous seven pages relates to the 327 Color schedules on the following pages for about 400 diagnosed (and obvious) health conditions. The Color schedules are excellent guides for tonating but they are not the "last word" as this must rest with you. Your best assistant for deciding how to proceed is the Table of Color Attributes (Chapter six), used with the attribute numbers in each schedule.

10. A representative Color schedule is shown below. Much of the information learned in previous Chapters is used in this diagram. Please study it carefully as successful use of the Color schedules may depend on it.

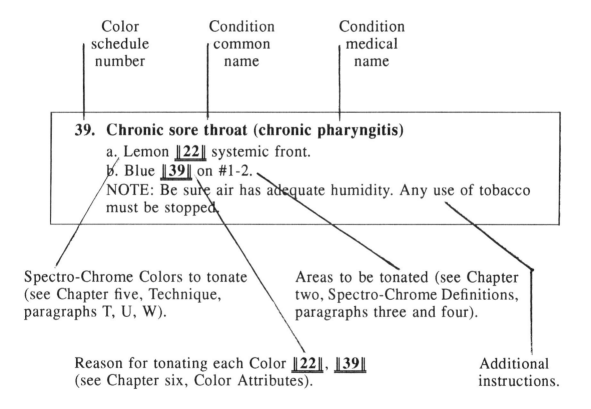

Color
schedule
number

Condition
common
name

Condition
medical
name

39. Chronic sore throat (chronic pharyngitis)
  a. Lemon ‖**22**‖ systemic front.
  b. Blue ‖**39**‖ on #1-2.
  NOTE: Be sure air has adequate humidity. Any use of tobacco must be stopped.

Spectro-Chrome Colors to tonate
(see Chapter five, Technique,
paragraphs T, U, W).

Areas to be tonated (see Chapter
two, Spectro-Chrome Definitions,
paragraphs three and four).

Reason for tonating each Color ‖**22**‖, ‖**39**‖
(see Chapter six, Color Attributes).

Additional
instructions.

11. If you put into practice everything learned to this point, you should be ready to proceed and give or take your first tonation.

Schedule
#:   Condition name:

1. **Aphasia, agnosia, apraxia, aphemia, anarthria, anosmia, agraphia, any loss of sensory ability due to sensory nerve impairment. Dyslexia**
   a. Lemon ‖22‖ systemic front.
   b. Sensory nervous system schedule (#275) on #1-15, or on affected area.
   -

2. **Acute encephalitis. Cerebral: abscess – aneurism – embolism – hemorrhage – thrombosis**
   a. Green ‖29-32‖ systemic front (Lemon ‖22‖ for embolism or throm-
   b. Indigo ‖44‖ on affected area.   bosis).
   c. Magenta ‖66‖ on #1-2-3-4-5, or Purple ‖56‖ if blood pressure is high.
   NOTE: If with paralysis also use Motor nervous system schedule (#276) on #1-15. In abscesses, aspiration may be necessary if encapsulation occurs (see Color schedule #296).
   -

3. **Cerebral tumors (see under tumors, #177)**
   a. Lemon ‖22‖ systemic front.
   b. Indigo ‖44‖ on affected area.
   NOTE: If with paralysis also use Motor nervous system schedule (#276) on #1-15.
   -

4. **Hydrocephalus**
   a. Lemon ‖22‖ and Indigo ‖44‖ systemic back and on #1.
   NOTE: If with paralysis also use Motor nervous system schedule (#276) on #1-15. Some congenital anomalies may require surgical correction.
   -

5. **Cerebral concussion**
   a. Purple ‖54-56‖ systemic front.
   b. Indigo ‖44‖ on #1-15.
      For convalescence:
   c. Lemon ‖22‖ systemic front.
   d. Magenta ‖66‖ on #1-2-3-4-5.
   -

6. **Falling hair (alopecia)**
   a. Orange ‖15‖ on affected area.
   b. Lemon ‖22‖ systemic front.
   c. Magenta ‖64-66‖ on #1-2-3-4-5.
   NOTE: Emotional factors as well as diseases may be involved and require attention.
   -

7. **Insomnia. Nervous headache from business pressure, tension, emotional stress, etc.**
   a. Violet ‖51‖ on #1. Purple ‖54‖ on #1-2-3-4-5 may be useful if pulse is throbbing or rate is high.

8. Migraine headache
   a. During attack, Purple ‖54‖ on #1-2-3-4-5. Scarlet ‖72‖ on #1 may be tried.
   b. Between attacks tonate Motor nervous system schedule (#276) systemic front.
   NOTE: Sensitivity to certain foods or need for eyeglasses may trigger attacks. Temporomandibular-joint disorder may be causal; see a knowledgeable dentist (orthodontist).

- -

9. Facial hemiatrophy
   a. Sensory nervous system schedule (#275) on #1.
   b. Green ‖31‖ on #1.

- -

10. Acromegaly
   a. Lemon ‖22‖ systemic front.
   b. Green ‖30‖ and Indigo ‖44‖ on #1.

- -

11. Meniere's syndrome (labyrinthine vertigo)
   a. Green ‖31‖ systemic front.
   b. Purple ‖57‖ on ears.
   NOTE: Other conditions may be involved: meningitis, tumors, arteriosclerosis, excessive salt in the diet, hypoglycemia, purpura, etc. Some forms of vertigo or dizziness may be from inflammations, eye disorders, low blood pressure, fatigue, allergies; nerve dysfunction would require Sensory nervous system schedule (#275) on the ears.

- -

12. Mastoiditis
   a. Green ‖31-32‖ systemic front to include affected area.
   b. Orange ‖15‖ and Blue ‖39‖ on affected area until it is draining freely; then stop Orange and Blue and tonate:
   c. Turquoise ‖33‖ on affected area until draining shows signs of stopping, then also tonate
   d. Indigo ‖44‖ on affected area.

- -

13. Choked disc (papilledema)
   a. Green ‖32‖ systemic front.
   b. Indigo ‖44‖ and Purple ‖56‖ on #1.
   c. Magenta ‖66‖ on #1-2-3-4-5.
   NOTE: Cause must be found and treated: brain tumor, high blood pressure, emphysema, etc.

- -

14. Cataract, incipient
   a. Lemon ‖22‖ systemic front.
   b. Sensory nervous system schedule (#275) on #1.
   c. Magenta ‖65‖ on #4-5.   (Continued on next page)

Color attribute number: ‖00‖. Tonation areas: #0-00.

NOTE: This is of doubtful value for mature cataracts but may be tried as it has been effective in a few cases. Hypoparathyroid condition may be involved.

_ _

15. **Glaucoma**
    a. Lemon ||22|| systemic front.
    b. Indigo ||44|| on #1.
    c. Magenta ||65-67|| on #4-5-18.
    NOTE: Have eye examinations to check on progress.

_ _

16. **Thrush (stomatitis, oral candidiasis)**
    a. Turquoise ||33|| systemic front and in mouth.
    NOTE: Stop use of tobacco and alcoholic drinks, Avoid hot foods, spices. Clean teeth, tongue and mouth carefully after meals.

_ _

17. **Tongue eczema (geographical tongue)**
    a. Lemon ||22|| systemic front and on tongue.
    b. Bluc ||37|| on #1 if tongue itches.
    NOTE: Diet may need improvement; avoid indigestion.

_ _

18. **Smoker's tongue or mouth (leukoplakia buccalis)**
    a. Turquoise ||33|| (or Lemon ||22|| if condition is chronic) systemic front and in mouth.
    NOTE: Stop use of tobacco and alcoholic drinks. Avoid hot foods, spices. Clean teeth, tongue and mouth carefully after meals. Vitamin deficiencies and other diseases may be involved.

_ _

19. **Gum diseases (gingivitis, periodontitis)**
    a. Turquoise ||33|| (or Lemon ||22|| if condition is chronic) systemic front.
    b. Indigo ||44|| on #1.
    NOTE: Have a dental examination. Vitamin deficiencies may be involved.

_ _

20. **Toothache. Teething**
    a. Indigo ||44-47|| or Purple ||54|| on #1.
    NOTE: Have a dental examination.

_ _

21. **Tooth extraction (exodontia)**
    a. Before extraction, Purple ||54|| on #1.
    b. After extraction, Turquoise ||33|| and Indigo ||44-47|| on #1.

_ _

22. **Tooth abscess (see #296)**
    a. Green ||32|| systemic front.
    b. Indigo ||44-47|| on #1.
    c. Orange ||15|| on #1 may help to open and/or drain abscess.
    d. Magenta ||65|| on #4-5.
    NOTE: Have a dental examination.

23. Loose teeth
a. Lemon ‖22‖ systemic front.
b. Indigo ‖44‖ on #1.

- -

24. Bad breath (fetor oris)
a. Lemon ‖22‖ systemic front until cause can be determined.
NOTE: Cause can be decayed teeth; constipation; catarrh and other diseases of the mouth, stomach, pharynx, tonsils, gums, lungs, etc. Clean teeth, tongue and mouth carefully after each meal.

- -

25. Excess saliva (ptyalism)
a. Lemon ‖22‖ systemic front.
b. Indigo ‖44‖ on #1.

- -

26. Dry mouth
a. Lemon ‖22‖ systemic front.
b. Yellow ‖18‖ on #1-2; Orange ‖15‖ may be tried.
NOTE: If associated with nervous temperament, also try Purple ‖54‖ or Violet ‖51‖ on #1.

- -

27. Mouth infection (oral sepsis)
a. Turquoise ‖33‖ systemic front and in mouth.
NOTE: Clean teeth, tongue and mouth carefully after each meal. Have a dental examination for decayed teeth, abscesses, etc.

- -

28. Salivary gland inflammation
a. Turquoise ‖33‖ on #1-2-3-4-5.
NOTE: Often associated with lack of oral hygiene, infectious fevers, etc.

- -

29. Cold (acute coryza, nasal catarrh)
a. Green ‖32‖ systemic front.
b. Blue ‖39‖ on #1-2-3. Turquoise ‖33‖ systemic front may be tried instead of Green and Blue.
NOTE: At the first sign of onset tonate Scarlet ‖71‖ once on #1-2-3-4-5; take deep breaths. Any use of tobacco must be stopped. Be sure air has adequate humidity.

- -

30. Chronic coryza
a. Lemon ‖22‖ on #1-2-3-4-5.
NOTE: Any use of tobacco must be stopped. Be sure air has adequate humidity.

Color attribute number: ‖00‖. Tonation areas: #0-00.

31. Hay fever
a. Lemon ‖22‖ systemic front.
b. Turquoise ‖33‖ or Blue ‖39‖ on #1 at acute times (runny nose, etc).
NOTE: Irrigate nostrils with slightly salty warm water three times a day during the hay fever (pollen) season. Any use of tobacco must be stopped. Tonations may be more effective when taken systemic from area #22.

----

32. Nosebleed (epistaxis)
a. Indigo ‖44‖ on #1.

----

33. Recurring nosebleeds
a. Lemon ‖22‖ systemic front.
b. Magenta ‖66‖ on #1-2-3-4-5.
c. Indigo ‖44‖ on #1 during episodes.
NOTE: Systemic diseases may be involved. Dry room air, and a deficient diet can be contributory.

----

34. Acute tonsillitis
a. Green ‖32‖ systemic front.
b. Blue ‖39‖ on #1-2, or systemic front if with high fever.
c. Purple ‖54-60‖ on #1-2-3-4-5 if with headache or high fever.
NOTE: Any use of tobacco must be stopped. Be sure air has adequate humidity.

----

35. Chronic tonsillitis
a. Lemon ‖22‖ systemic front.
NOTE: Any use of tobacco must be stopped. Be sure air has adequate humidity.

----

36. Suppurative tonsillitis (quinsy)
a. Green ‖32‖ systemic front.
b. Indigo ‖44-45‖ on #1-2.
c. Lemon ‖22‖ systemic front after acute (febrile) stage has passed.
NOTE: Any use of tobacco must be stopped. Be sure air has adequate humidity.

----

37. Smoker's or speaker's throat (pharyngeal hyperemia)
a. Indigo ‖47‖ #1-2.
NOTE: Any use of tobacco must be stopped. Be sure air has adequate humidity.

----

38. Sore throat (acute pharyngitis)
a. Green ‖32‖ systemic front.
b. Blue ‖39‖ on #1-2.
NOTE: Any use of tobacco must be stopped. Be sure air has adequate humidity.

39. Chronic sore throat (chronic pharyngitis)

a. Lemon ‖**22**‖ systemic front.

b. Blue ‖**39**‖ on #1-2

NOTE: Any use of tobacco must be stopped. Be sure air has adequate humidity.

- -

40. Adenoids, hypertrophy of

a. Lemon ‖**22**‖ systemic front.

b. Indigo ‖**44**‖ on #1.

c. Orange ‖**15**‖ on #1 may be tried (see #177).

NOTE: Condition may be caused or aggravated by food or other allergies, or an infection.

- -

41. Wryneck (torticollis)

a. Motor nervous system schedule (#276) systemic back.

b. Violet ‖**49**‖ or Orange ‖**9**‖ may be tried on the affected area during a spasm attack.

- -

42. Acute laryngitis

a. Turquoise ‖**33**‖ systemic front.

b. Violet ‖**51**‖ on #1-2-3 also may be used if throat is painful.

NOTE: Any use of tobacco must be stopped. Be sure air has adequate humidity.

- -

43. Chronic laryngitis

a. Lemon ‖**22**‖ systemic front.

b. Blue ‖**39**‖ on #1-2-3.

NOTE: Any use of tobacco must be stopped. Be sure air has adequate humidity.

- -

44. Edematous laryngitis

a. Magenta ‖**66**‖ on #1-2-3-4-5.

b. Scarlet ‖**70-75**‖ on #18.

c. Turquoise ‖**33**‖ systemic front.

   For convalescence:

d. Lemon ‖**22**‖ systemic front.

e. Magenta ‖**66**‖ on #1-2-3-4-5.

NOTE: Condition can become critical in a very short time. High humidity is a must. Any use of tobacco must be stopped.

- -

45. Child-crowing (spasmodic laryngitis)

a. Lemon ‖**22**‖ systemic front.

b. Indigo ‖**47**‖ on #1-2-3.

c. Orange ‖**9**‖ on areas of spasms.

Color attribute number: ‖**00**‖. Tonation areas: #0-00.

46. Tuberculous laryngitis
   a. Turquoise ‖33‖ systemic front, followed by Lemon ‖22‖ when there is little fever.
   b. Orange ‖6-15‖ on #1-2-3-4-5 when there is little fever.
   NOTE: Any use of tobacco must be stopped. Be sure air has adequate humidity.

- -

47. Acute bronchitis
   a. Turquoise ‖33‖ systemic front.
   b. Violet ‖51‖ or Purple ‖63‖ on #1-2-3-4-5 during dry cough stage (refer to attribute ‖63‖).
   NOTE: Any use of tobacco must be stopped. Be sure air has adequate humidity.

- -

48. Chronic or fibrinous bronchitis
   a. Lemon ‖22‖ systemic front.
   b. Blue ‖39‖ on #4-5.
   c. Violet ‖51‖ on #1-2-3-4-5, or Purple ‖63‖ if there is a dry cough (Indigo ‖44‖ and Purple if hemorrhage occurs; refer to attribute ‖63‖. For convalescence:
   d. Lemon ‖22‖ systemic front.
   e. Yellow ‖17‖ on #4-5-17 followed by Orange ‖15‖.
   f. Conclude with Turquoise ‖36‖ systemic front.

- -

49. Hiccup (singultus)
   a. Orange ‖9‖ #6-7-8-9.
   b. Indigo ‖47‖ on #16.
   c. May also try: 1) Breathe into a paper (not plastic) bag for a minute or two. 2) Rotate and hold the head as far as possible to the left, then take two or three swallows of water. 3) Cause sneezing. 4) Pull firmly on the tongue.
   NOTE: Persistent hiccups are sometimes associated with tumors, inflammations, abdominal disorders, alcoholism, etc.

- -

50. Pharyngeal ulceration
   a. Lemon ‖22‖ systemic front
   b. Blue ‖39‖ on #1-2-3.

- -

51. Neck cellulitis
   a. Green ‖32‖ systemic front.
   b. Blue ‖39‖ on #1-2-3.

- -

52. Acute esophagitis
   a. Green ‖32‖ systemic front.
   b. Blue ‖39‖ on #2-3-4-5-8.
   NOTE: Avoid hot or spicy foods. Do not use tobacco products or alcoholic drinks in any form.

53. Chronic esophagitis.
a. Lemon ‖22‖ systemic front.
b. Blue ‖39‖ on #2-3-4-5-8.
NOTE: Avoid hot or spicy foods. Do not use tobacco products or alcoholic drinks in any form.

- -

54. Foodpipe spasm (esophagismus)
a. Lemon ‖22‖ systemic front.
b. Orange ‖9‖ on #2-3-4-5-8.
c. A nervous person may try Violet ‖49‖ or Purple ‖54‖ on #1.
NOTE: May be associated with epilepsy, chorea, etc.

- -

55. Esophageal cancer (see schedule #177)
a. Lemon ‖22‖ systemic front.
b. Indigo ‖44‖ on #2-3-4-5-8.

- -

56. Thyroidal congestion
a. Green ‖29‖ systemic front.
b. Blue ‖39‖ on #3.
c. Magenta ‖66‖ on #3-4-5.

- -

57. Thyroiditis
a. Green ‖32‖ systemic front.
b. Blue ‖39‖ on #3 or Indigo ‖44-45‖ if purulent.

- -

58. Dwarfism, infantilism
a. Lemon ‖22-24‖ systemic front, and if with dysfunction of:
b. Pituitary–Green ‖38‖ on #1 (and schedule #177 if brain tumor is present).
c. Thyroid–see schedule #60, hypothyroidism.
d. Heart–see appropriate heart condition schedule.
e. Digestion–Yellow ‖18‖ on #6-7-8-9-10.
f. Kidneys–see appropriate kidney condition schedule.
g. Bone development–Orange ‖14‖ systemic front from area #22.
NOTE: Dietary, emotional, and other factors may be involved.

- -

59. Simple goiter (thyroid hypertrophy)
a. Orange ‖7‖ and Lemon ‖22‖ systemic front.
b. Green ‖30‖ on #1.
c. Indigo ‖44‖ on #3.

- -

60. Thyroid underactivity (hypothyroidism), myxedema, cretinism
a. Orange ‖7-15‖ and Lemon ‖22‖ systemic front.
b. Green ‖30‖ on #1

Color attribute number: ‖00‖. Tonation areas: #0-00.

61. Thyroid overactivity (hyperthyroidism). Exophthalmic goiter (Graves' disease)
   a. Lemon ‖**22**‖ and Indigo ‖**44-47**‖ systemic front.
   b. Green ‖**30**‖ on #1.
   c. Purple ‖**58**‖ on #4-5, or systemic front (‖**56**‖) if blood pressure is high (see schedule #277).
   NOTE: The cause is unknown but condition may be triggered by physical or emotional stress.

- -

62. Thyroid tumor (see #177)
   a. Lemon ‖**22**‖ systemic front.
   b. Indigo ‖**44**‖ on #3.

- -

63. Parathyroid underactivity (hypoparathyroidism), parathyroid tetany
   a. Lemon ‖**22-27**‖ systemic front.
   b. Indigo ‖**41**‖ on #3.
   c. Orange ‖**9**‖ on affected areas may be tried during spasms.
   NOTE: Increase in dietary calcium and vitamin D may be needed.

- -

64. Parathyroid overactivity (hyperparathyroidism), osteitis fibrosa cystica
   a. Lemon ‖**22-24**‖ and Orange ‖**8-14**‖ systemic front.
   NOTE: Increase in dietary calcium, phosphorus, and vitamin D is likely to be needed. Other diseases may be involved such as pancreatitis. Some cancers exhibit similar symptoms.

- -

65. Acute carditis
   a. Turquoise ‖**33**‖ systemic front.
   b. Magenta ‖**65**‖ on #4-5.
   c. Indigo ‖**44**‖ on #4-5 if with effusion.

- -

66. Chronic carditis
   a. Lemon ‖**22**‖ systemic front.
   b. Magenta ‖**65**‖ on #4-5.
   c. Indigo ‖**44**‖ on #4-5 if with effusion.

- -

67. Cardiac: dilatation–hypertrophy–regurgitation–insufficiency (incompetency)
   a. Lemon ‖**22**‖ systemic front.
   b. Magenta ‖**65-66**‖ and Indigo ‖**44**‖ on #4-5.
   c. In regurgitation and insufficiency, Scarlet ‖**71**‖ on #4-5 also may be tonated if blood pressure is not too high.

- -

68. Cardiac valvular stenosis
   a. Lemon ‖**22**‖ systemic front.
   b. Magenta ‖**65**‖ on #4-5.
   (Continued on next page)

    c. Scarlet ‖**71**‖ on #4-5 also may be tonated if blood pressure is not too high.

- -

69a. Aortic aneurism
    a. Lemon ‖**22**‖ and Purple ‖**55**‖ systemic front.
    b. Indigo ‖**44**‖ and Magenta ‖**65-66**‖ on #4-5.

- -

69b. Multiple arterial aneurisms (periarterial nodosa)
    a. Turquoise ‖**33**‖ systemic front and back if with fever, or
    b. Lemon ‖**22**‖ systemic front and back if with little or no fever.
    c. Purple ‖**54-56-60**‖ systemic front.
    d. Magenta ‖**65-66-67**‖ on #4-5-18.
    e. Red ‖**2**‖ on #7-8 if liver is involved.
NOTE: This disease is extremely serious. Any organ of the body may be affected and require attention.

- -

70. Fatty heart
    a. Lemon ‖**22**‖ systemic front.
    b. Orange ‖**15**‖ and Indigo ‖**44**‖ on #4-5.

- -

71. Cardiac arrhythmia
    a. Lemon ‖**22**‖ and Magenta ‖**65-66**‖ systemic front. In some cases tonating systemic from area #22 may be more effective, and even essential.
    b. Orange or Indigo systemic front may be required if cardiac Q-T duration (refractory period) is abnormal due to calcium imbalance.
NOTE: Dietary intake of calcium and/or potassium may need modification.

- -

72. Rapid heart (tachycardia)
    a. Turquoise ‖**33**‖ and Magenta ‖**65-66**‖ systemic front.
    b. Purple ‖**53-58**‖ on #4-5-18.
NOTE: Tonating systemic front and back from area #22 may be more effective and even essential. After condition is stabilized, tonate Lemon ‖**22**‖ instead of Turquoise.

- -

73. Slow heart (bradycardia)
    a. Lemon ‖**22**‖ and Magenta ‖**65-66**‖ on #4-5-18.
    b. Scarlet ‖**72**‖ on #4-5-18 if blood pressure is not too high.
NOTE: Tonating systemic front and back from area #22 may be more effective and even essential.

74. Angina pectoris
    a. Lemon ‖22‖ and Magenta ‖65-66‖ systemic front.
    b. Purple ‖57‖ on #4-5 during paroxysms.
    NOTE: Other diseases may be involved and require attention: gastric, cardiac, vascular, prostatic, etc.

- -

75. Tuberculosis (pulmonary phthisis). Scrofula (lymphatic tuberculosis)
    When there is little or no fever:
    a. Lemon ‖22‖ and Orange ‖6-15‖ systemic front.
    b. Orange ‖6‖ on #17 (not used in scrofula).
    c. Indigo ‖44-45‖ on areas of suppuration or effusion.
    d. Purple ‖63‖ on #4-5 if with pulmonary hemorrhage (see attrib. ‖63‖).
    When there is fever:
    e. Stop tonating Lemon and Orange.
    f. Depending on fever level:
    Turquoise ‖33‖ systemic front, or
    Green ‖32‖ and Blue ‖39‖ systemic front.
    g. Purple ‖60‖ on #4-5 if fever is high; systemic front if very high.
    h. Indigo ‖44-45‖ on areas of suppuration or effusion.
    i. Purple ‖63‖ on #4-5 if with pulmonary hemorrhage (see attrib. ‖63‖).
    NOTE: All Colors also may be tonated on #17 if case is critical.

- -

76. Pneumonia
    a. Green ‖32‖ systemic front.
    b. Blue ‖39‖ on #4-5-17.
    c. Magenta ‖65‖ on #4-5, or
    d. Scarlet ‖72‖ systemic front and back if
    circulatory failure appears imminent.
    e. Purple ‖60-63‖ on #4-5 if fever is high, or blood is present in sputum (see attribute ‖63‖).
    For convalescence:
    f. Magenta ‖65-67‖ on #4-5-18.
    g. Lemon ‖22‖ systemic front followed by Yellow ‖17‖ and then Orange ‖6‖.
    h. Conclude with Turquoise ‖36‖ systemic front.
    NOTE: Any use of tobacco must be stopped.

- -

77. Bronchiectasis
    a. Orange ‖6-15‖ and Lemon ‖22‖ systemic front and on #17.
    b. Purple ‖63‖ on #4-5 if with pulmonary hemorrhage (see attrib. ‖63‖).
    NOTE: May be associated with cystic fibrosis, pneumonia, etc. Any use of tobacco must be stopped.

78. Asthma

During an attack:

a. Purple ‖**54-57-58**‖ on #1-2-3-4-5.

b. Scarlet ‖**70**‖ on #18.

c. Orange ‖**9**‖ may be tried.

Between attacks:

d. Lemon ‖**22**‖ systemic front.

e. Orange ‖**6-15**‖ on #2-3-4-5.

f. Magenta ‖**64-65-67**‖ on #4-5-18.

NOTE: Emotional factors are often involved. In some cases certain dusts, proteins, fumes, etc. may precipitate an attack. Any use of tobacco must be stopped.

- -

79. Acute lung congestion

a. Turquoise ‖**33**‖ systemic front.

b. Blue ‖**39**‖ on #17.

c. Magenta ‖**65**‖ on #4-5.

NOTE: Be sure air has adequate humidity. Any use of tobacco must be stopped.

- -

80. Hemoptysis

a. Green ‖**32**‖ systemic front.

b. Indigo ‖**44**‖ and Purple ‖**63**‖ on #4-5-17 (see attribute ‖**63**‖).

NOTE: Often associated with other disorders which must be resolved if present. Any use of tobacco must be stopped.

- -

81. Asbestosis – blacklung – emphysema – silicosis (pneumoconiosis)

a. Lemon ‖**22-23**‖ systemic front.

b. Orange ‖**6-15**‖ and Yellow ‖**17**‖ on #4-5-17.

NOTE: Information in schedule #75 also may apply to these disorders. Be sure air has adequate humidity. Any use of tobacco must be stopped.

- -

82. Lung gangrene

a. Lemon ‖**22**‖ systemic front and on #17 (or Green ‖**32**‖ and Blue ‖**39**‖ if with fever).

b. Magenta ‖**65**‖ on #4-5 (or Purple ‖**60**‖ if fever is high).

c. Indigo ‖**44**‖ and Purple ‖**63**‖ on #4-5-17 if lung hemorrhage occurs (refer to attribute ‖**63**‖).

For convalescence:

d. Lemon ‖**22**‖ systemic front.

e. Orange ‖**6**‖ on #4-5-17.

f. Conclude with Turquoise ‖**36**‖ systemic front.

NOTE: Air must have adequate humidity. Stop any use of tobacco.

Color attribute number: ‖**00**‖. Tonation areas: #0-00.

83. Lung abscess (see #296, abscess)
 a. Green ‖**32**‖ systemic front.
 b. Indigo ‖**44**‖ on #4-5-17.
 c. Magenta ‖**65**‖ on #4-5 (or Blue ‖**39**‖ systemic front and Purple ‖**60**‖ on #4-5 if fever is high).
 NOTE: Be sure air has adequate humidity. Any use of tobacco must be stopped.

- -

84. Lung growths (pulmonary carcinoma) – (see #177, cancer)
 a. Lemon ‖**22**‖ systemic front.
 b. Indigo ‖**44**‖ on #4-5-17.
 c. Purple ‖**63**‖ on #4-5 if with pulmonary hemorrhage (see attrib. ‖**63**‖).
 NOTE: Any use of tobacco must be stopped.

- -

85. Acute pleurisy
 a. Green ‖**32**‖ systemic front.
 b. Blue ‖**39**‖ on #4-5-17, or Indigo ‖**44**‖ if effusion occurs.
 c. Magenta ‖**65-67**‖ on #4-5-18
 d. Violet ‖**51**‖ on #4-5 may be tonated if pain is severe.

- -

86. Chronic pleurisy
 a. Lemon ‖**22**‖ systemic front and on #17.
 b. Indigo ‖**44**‖ on #4-5-17 if effusion occurs.
 NOTE: Underlying cause must be found and tonated.

- -

87. Purulent pleurisy (empyema of the chest)
 a. Green ‖**32**‖ systemic front.
 b. Indigo ‖**44-45**‖ on #4-5-17.
 c. Magenta ‖**65-67**‖ on #4-5-18.

- -

88. Hydrothorax
 a. Green ‖**31-32**‖ systemic front.
 b. Indigo ‖**44**‖ on #4-5.
 c. Magenta ‖**67**‖ on #18.

- -

89. Thymus hypertrophy
 a. Lemon ‖**22**‖ systemic front.
 b. Indigo ‖**44**‖ on #4-5 (thymus).

- -

90. Thymus atrophy
 a. Lemon ‖**22-26**‖ systemic front.

- -

91. Thymus abscess (see #296, abscess)
 a. Green ‖**32**‖ systemic front.
 b. Indigo ‖**44-45**‖ on #4-5 (thymus).
 c. Magenta ‖**65**‖ on #4-5.

92. Status thymicolymphaticus, lymphatism
  a. Yellow ||17||, Lemon ||22||, and Magenta ||66|| systemic front.
  b. Indigo ||44|| on #4-5 (thymus).

- -

93. Jaundice (icterus)
  a. Lemon ||22|| systemic front.
  b. Red ||2|| on #7-8.
  c. Yellow ||18-20|| on #6-7-8-9-10.
  d. Magenta ||65-66|| on #4-5-6-7-8-18.
  NOTE: Other conditions may be involved: ascites (schedule #115), gallstones (#98), hepatitis (#97b). Avoid all alcoholic drinks.

- -

94. Liver cancer (see #177, cancer)
  a. Lemon ||22|| systemic front.
  b. Indigo ||44|| on #7-8.

- -

95. Fatty liver
  a. Green ||29-31|| systemic front.
  b. Red ||2|| on #7-8.
  NOTE: Underlying cause can be a poor diet, drugs, obesity, chemical poisoning, alcoholism, etc., which also must be treated.

- -

96. Waxy liver (amyloid liver)
  a. Green ||29-31|| systemic front.
  b. Red ||2|| on #7-8.
  c. Indigo ||44|| on #7-8 and areas with suppuration.
  NOTE: Underlying cause can be: syphilis, bone disease, rickets, tuberculosis, etc., which also must be treated.

- -

97a. Acute hepatitis
  a. Green ||32|| and Blue ||39|| systemic front.
  b. Red ||2|| on #7-8.
  NOTE: A well-balanced diet is essential. Avoid all alcoholic drinks.

- -

97b. Chronic hepatitis, liver cirrhosis
  a. Lemon ||22|| systemic front.
  b. Red ||2|| on #7-8.
  c. Magenta ||65-69|| on #4-5-6-7-8-18.
  d. Indigo ||44|| on affected areas if ascites or hemorrhages occur.
  NOTE: A well-balanced diet is essential. Avoid all alcoholic drinks.

Color attribute number: ||00||. Tonation areas: #0-00.

98. Gallstones (cholelithiasis)
a. Lemon ‖22‖ systemic front.
b. Orange ‖15‖ on #7-8.
NOTE: Gallstones may have to be removed, depending on their quantity and size.

- -

99. Malignant jaundice (icterus gravis)
a. Green ‖31‖ and Indigo ‖44‖ systemic front.
b. Red ‖2‖ on #7-8.
NOTE: Underlying cause can be any of several serious disorders.

- -

100. Acute gastritis
a. Orange ‖12‖ on #6-8 once, then
b. Turquoise ‖33‖ systemic front, and
c. Indigo ‖44‖ on #6-8.
NOTE: It may be useful to treat initially with schedule #105. Use a liquid diet or water only for a day or two.

- -

101. Chronic gastritis
a. Lemon ‖22‖ systemic front.
b. Orange ‖11‖ on #6-8.
NOTE: Other disorders may be involved. Have a dental examination. Watch diet carefully.

- -

102. Stomach cancer (see #177, cancer)
a. Lemon ‖22‖ systemic front.
b. Indigo ‖44‖ on #6-8.

- -

103. Peptic ulcers. Stomach bleeding and vomiting (hematemesis)
a. Lemon ‖22‖ systemic front.
b. Indigo ‖44‖ on #6-8.
NOTE: Other disorders may be involved or develop and must be treated.

- -

104. Cholera infantum
a. Green ‖29-32‖ and Indigo ‖44‖ systemic front.
b. Purple ‖54-60‖ on #4-5.
    As symptoms subside:
c. Turquoise ‖33‖ systemic front.
d. Magenta ‖65‖ on #4-5.
    For convalescence:
e. Lemon ‖22‖ systemic front, followed by Yellow ‖17‖.
f. Conclude with Turquoise ‖36‖ systemic front.
NOTE: Give only water (electrolytes may need to be adjusted) or fruit juices (if tolerated) for no more than two or three days, until acute symptoms subside; extreme caution must be exercised in this regard.

105. Vomiting (emesis)

a. Drink water, immediately tonate Orange ‖12‖ on #6-8; repeat until vomit is only water (see Note).

b. Indigo ‖44-47‖ on #6-8 to stop retching.

NOTE: Vomiting *must not* be encouraged if poisoned by gasoline, turpentine, acids, washing soda, etc. In such cases, contact nearest poison-control center and begin first-aid measures.

- -

106. Indigestion, flatulence (gas)

a. Orange ‖13‖ on #6-7-8-9-10.

NOTE: If tonated soon after eating, vomiting may result which is often beneficial.

- -

107. Diarrhea (catarrhal enteritis)

a. Yellow ‖19‖ on #6-7-8-9-10 one tonation, then Turquoise ‖33‖ systemic front, and

b. Indigo ‖44-45-47‖ on #6-7-8-9-10 if condition does not begin to abate in one day.

NOTE: Use a liquid diet or water only for a day or two, until condition subsides. **If electrolyte loss or dehydration is severe, immediate attention may be essential.**

- -

108. Appendicitis

a. Green ‖31-32‖ systemic front.

b. Blue ‖39‖ and Indigo ‖44-45-47‖ on #9-10.

NOTE: Use a liquid diet or water only for a few days until condition subsides. **If electrolyte loss or dehydration is severe, immediate attention may be essential.**

- -

109. Constipation (costiveness)

a. Lemon ‖22-27‖ systemic front.

b. Yellow ‖18-19‖ on #6-7-8-9-10, also Orange ‖11-13-15‖ if condition does not respond.

NOTE: Colors also may be tonated on #18-19. See Chapter five, part one, paragraphs c through i, and q. Diet probably needs improvement. In an occasional case, emotional factors may be involved; if so, try Violet ‖51‖ or Purple ‖54‖ on #1 (or systemic front).

- -

110. Enteroptosis

a. Lemon ‖22‖ and Indigo ‖44‖ on #6-7-8-9-10.

b. Yellow ‖16‖ systemic front.

NOTE: An abdominal support may be necessary in some cases.

Color attribute number: ‖00‖. Tonation areas: #0-00.

111. Worm infestations: tape – hook – round - filariasis.
Trichinosis. Intestinal and other parasites
   a. Yellow ‖21‖ and Lemon ‖22‖ systemic to include affected areas.
   b. Green ‖31-32‖ systemic front during acute stage.
   c. Blue ‖39‖ systemic front if fever occurs.
   NOTE: Most worms enter through the mouth (poor sanitary and food pre-paration habits, biting fingernails, etc.). Tonate symptoms as they occur.

- -

112. Dysentery, colitis, acute gastroenteritis
   a. Green ‖31-32‖ systemic front.
   b. Yellow ‖19‖ on #6-7-8-9-10 once or twice to empty bowels, then
   c. Indigo ‖44‖ on #6-7-8-9-10.
   NOTE: Use a liquid diet or water only for a day or two, until condition subsides. In colitis, emotional problems and overeating are often involved and must be corrected. **If electrolyte loss or dehydration is severe, im-mediate attention may be essential.**

- -

113. Acute peritonitis
   a. Green ‖32‖ systemic front.
   b. Blue ‖39‖ and Indigo ‖44-45-47‖ on #6-7-8-9-10.
   c. Magenta ‖65‖ on #4-5, or Purple ‖58-60‖ if with high fever or rapid pulse.
   NOTE: **If electrolyte loss or dehydration is severe, immediate attention may be essential.**

- -

114. Chronic peritonitis
   a. Lemon ‖22‖ systemic front.
   NOTE: Treat complications as they occur.

- -

115. Ascites
   a. Green ‖29‖ systemic front.
   b. Indigo ‖44‖ on #6-7-8-9-10.
   c. Magenta ‖65‖ on #4-5.
   d. Scarlet ‖70‖ on #18.
   NOTE: Often associated with other disorders, liver disease being the most common.

- -

116. Acute pancreatitis
   a. Turquoise ‖33‖ systemic front.
   b. Blue ‖39‖ and Indigo ‖44-47‖ on #6-7-8-18.
   c. Magenta ‖65‖ on #4-5.
   NOTE: Intravenous fluids may be required, depending on severity of the case.

117. Chronic pancreatitis
a. Lemon ‖**22-27**‖ systemic front and on #18.
b. Yellow ‖**18**‖ on #6-8.
NOTE: May require tonations listed for acute pancreatitis (#116) until acute symptoms subside.

- -

118. Pancreatic cancer (see #177, cancer)
a. Lemon ‖**22**‖ systemic front and on #18.
b. Indigo ‖**44**‖ on #6-8-18.

- -

119. Low blood sugar (hypoglycemia, chronic hyperinsulinism)
a. Lemon ‖**22**‖ systemic front, and if with dysfunction of:
   b. Pituitary–Green ‖**30**‖ on #1.
   c. Thyroid–Orange ‖**7**‖ on #3.
   d. Liver–Red ‖**2**‖ on #7-8.
   e. Pancreas (overactivity, high insulin)–Violet ‖**49**‖ on #6-8-18,
         (underactivity, low glucagon)–Yellow ‖**18**‖ on #6-8-18.
   f. Digestive tract–Yellow ‖**18**‖ on #6-7-8-9-10.
   g. Kidneys–Magenta ‖**69**‖ on #18.
   h. Adrenal and chromaffin system–Scarlet ‖**70-71**‖ systemic front and back.
NOTE: Improved diet is usually required. Avoid alcoholic drinks and all forms of refined sugar. Vitamin deficiencies may be involved. Emotional burdens also may have to be moderated.

- -

120. Diabetes mellitus
a. Lemon ‖**22**‖ systemic front.
b. Yellow ‖**16**‖ on #6-7-8-9-10.
c. Magenta ‖**66**‖ systemic front from #22.
NOTE: Any of several conditions may contribute to the development of this disease; the diet is especially important in controlling it. Lack of chromium in the diet, or its assimilation, has been implicated. Avoid all forms of refined sugar and excessively sweet foods. Several small meals a day instead of the usual three large meals may sharply reduce bodily needs for insulin. Mental strain and anxiety, as well as type of diet, may have a marked influence on the course of this disease.

- -

121. Glucose in the urine (glycosuria)
a. Lemon ‖**22**‖ systemic front, and if with dysfunction of:
   b. Pituitary–Green ‖**30**‖ on #1.
   c. Pancreas–Yellow ‖**18**‖ on #6-8-18.
   d. Kidneys–Magenta ‖**69**‖ on #18.

Color attribute number: ‖**00**‖. Tonation areas: #0-00.

122. Diabetes insipidus
   a. Lemon ‖22‖ systemic front.
   b. Green ‖30‖ on #1.
   c. Orange ‖7‖ on #3.
   d. Indigo ‖44‖ on #1-15 if with cerebral tumor.
   e. Magenta ‖69‖ on #18.

- -

123. Splenic abscess (see #296, abscess)
   a. Green ‖32‖ systemic front.
   b. Indigo ‖44‖ on #6.
   c. Magenta ‖65‖ on #4-5-6-7-8.

- -

124. Banti's disease
   a. Lemon ‖22‖ systemic front.
   b. Red ‖3‖ systemic front from #22.
   b. Indigo ‖44‖ on #6, and on hemorrhages if they occur.
   c. Magenta ‖66‖ on #4-5-6-7-8.
   NOTE: Other diseases are usually involved and must be treated.

- -

125. Gonorrhea
   a. Green ‖32‖ and Blue ‖39‖ systemic front until acute symptoms or apparent effects of the disease disappear, then
   b. Lemon ‖22‖ and Yellow ‖17‖ systemic front for several weeks (see #280, carrier).

- -

126. Syphilis
   a. Green ‖32‖ and Magenta ‖66‖ systemic front and back for three weeks with
   b. Blue ‖39‖ systemic front for three weeks, then
   c. Lemon ‖22‖, Yellow ‖17‖ and Magenta ‖66‖ systemic front and back. Continue tonations for several weeks after all symptoms disappear (or for several months if condition is long-standing; see schedule #280).
   d. Conclude with Turquoise ‖36‖ systemic front.

- -

127. Chancre
   For three weeks:
   a. Green ‖32‖ and Magenta ‖66‖ systemic front and back.
   b. Blue ‖39‖ on affected area.
   After three weeks:
   c. Yellow ‖17‖, Lemon ‖22‖ and Magenta ‖66‖ systemic front and back.
   d. Orange ‖15‖ on the affected area until it begins to close, then
   e. Turquoise ‖35-36‖ systemic front for a week, then add
   f. Indigo ‖44‖ on the affected area.
   (Continued on next page)

    g. Tonate (e) and (f) until area is healed.

    h. Conclude with Green ‖29‖ systemic front.

- -

128. Whites (leukorrhea)

    a. Lemon ‖22‖ systemic front.

    b. Indigo ‖44-45‖ on #10-11.

    c. Magenta ‖65‖ on #4-5.

NOTE: See schedule #314 if condition is chronic.

- -

129. Lack of menstruation (amenorrhea)

    a. Lemon ‖22‖ systemic front.

    b. Green ‖30‖ on #1.

    c. Scarlet ‖78‖ on #10-11.

    d. Magenta ‖67‖ on #18.

NOTE: Possible causes: Thyroid dysfunction, excessive exercise, diabetes, some drugs, emotional stress.

- -

130. Menstrual cramps

    a. Orange ‖9‖ on #10-11.

    b. Scarlet ‖70‖ on #18.

       Between menstrual periods:

    c. Lemon ‖22‖ systemic front.

    d. Magenta ‖64-66-67-68‖ systemic front and on #18.

- -

131. Painful menstruation or excessive flow. Falling womb

       During menstrual period:

    a. Indigo ‖44-47‖ on #10-11.

       Between menstrual periods:

    b. Lemon ‖22‖ systemic front.

    c. Magenta ‖64-66-68‖ systemic front and on #18.

    d. For falling womb also tonate Indigo ‖44‖ on #10-11.

- -

132. Tendency to miscarry

    a. Lemon ‖22‖ systemic front.

    b. Green ‖30‖ on #1.

    c. Magenta ‖64-67-68‖ systemic front and on #18.

    d. Scarlet ‖78‖ on #18.

NOTE: Refrain from marital relations for these weeks. Do not wear high-heeled shoes.

Color attribute number: ‖00‖. Tonation areas: #0-00.__

133. Sexual: impotence/sterility/apathy
   a. Green ‖**29-30**‖ and Orange ‖**15**‖ systemic front.
   b. Magenta ‖**64-66-67**‖ systemic front and on #18.
   c. Scarlet ‖**77-78**‖ on #10-11.
   NOTE: Emotional factors may be involved and require attention.

- -

134. Excessive sexual craving
   a. Turquoise ‖**33-34**‖ systemic front.
   b. Purple ‖**62**‖ on #10-11-18.
   c. Magenta ‖**64-66-68**‖ systemic front.
   NOTE: Emotional factors may be involved and require attention.

- -

135. Vomiting in pregnancy
   a. Turquoise ‖**33**‖ systemic front.
   b. Indigo ‖**47**‖ on #9.

- -

136. Spotting from impending miscarriage
   a. Green ‖**29-30**‖ systemic front.
   b. Indigo ‖**44**‖ on #10-11.
   NOTE: Refrain from marital relations. Do not wear high-heeled shoes. Bed-rest until danger passes has been recommended but its value has been questioned and is being studied. Cautious exercise may follow.

- -

137. Normal pregnancy
   Occasionally tonate:
   a. Green ‖**29**‖ systemic front.
   b. Yellow ‖**18**‖ on #6-7-8-9-10.
   c. Magenta ‖**65-67**‖ on #4-5-18.

- -

138. Abortion
   There is no Spectro-Chrome Color which will cause an abortion but if a spontaneous abortion is inevitable due to natural circumstances, tonate these Colors to help precipitate the event and lessen the likelihood of untoward after-effects:
   a. Green ‖**30-32**‖ systemic front.
   b. Scarlet ‖**76-78**‖ on #10-11.
   After the abortion:
   c. Indigo ‖**46**‖ on #4-5 if milk flow begins.
   d. If blood flow is excessive, see schedule #140.

- -

139. Pregnancy: long labor–slow placental separation–weak contractions
   a. Green ‖**30**‖ on #1.
   b. Scarlet ‖**76-78**‖ on #10-11.

140. Pregnancy: excessive flow after delivery
   a. Scarlet ‖78‖ on #10-11 (placenta must be expelled), followed by
   b. Indigo ‖44‖ on #10-11.
      After flow is controlled
   c. Green ‖29‖ and Magenta ‖64‖ systemic front.

- -

141. Pregnancy: to regulate milk production
   a. Green ‖29‖ systemic front, and
   b. Orange ‖10‖ on #4-5 to increase production, or
   c. Indigo ‖46‖ on #4-5 to decrease production.
   NOTE: Use care in dietary habits.

- -

142. Prostate enlargement (benign prostatic hypertrophy)
   a. Lemon ‖22‖ systemic front.
   b. Orange ‖15‖ and Indigo ‖44‖ between #11 and #19.
   NOTE: Lack of zinc in the diet has been implicated. Wheat germ is a good source of zinc but it is better to eliminate white-flour from the diet and use only whole-wheat products.

- -

143. Acute prostatic inflammation
   a. Turquoise ‖33‖ systemic front.
   b. Blue ‖39‖ between #11 and #19.
   NOTE: Lack of zinc in the diet has been implicated. Wheat germ is a good source of zinc but it is better to eliminate white-flour from the diet and use only whole-wheat products.

- -

144. Chronic prostatic inflammation
   a. Lemon ‖22‖ systemic front and between #11 and #19.
   b. If enlargement has occurred use schedule #142.
   NOTE: Lack of zinc in the diet has been implicated. Wheat germ is a good source of zinc but it is better to eliminate white-flour from the diet and use only whole-wheat products.

- -

145. Acute nephritis
   a. Turquoise ‖33‖ systemic back.
   b. Magenta ‖66‖ systemic front.
   c. Scarlet ‖70‖ on #18, or Magenta ‖69‖ if blood pressure is too high.

- -

146. Chronic nephritis, renal sclerosis, uremia
   a. Lemon ‖22‖ systemic back.
   b. Magenta ‖66‖ systemic front.
   c. Scarlet ‖70‖ on #18, or Magenta ‖69‖ if blood pressure is too high.
   NOTE: Arteriosclerosis and other complications may be involved and require attention.

Color attribute number: ‖00‖. Tonation areas: #0-00.

147. Urine suppression (prerenal anuria)
   a. Green ||30-32|| systemic back.
   b. Scarlet ||70|| on #18.
   NOTE: Obstructive suppression may require surgical intervention.

- -

148. Blood in urine (hematuria)
       If bleeding is from the bladder:
   a. Grccn ||31-32|| systemic front.
   b. Indigo ||44|| on #10.
       If bleeding is from the kidneys:
   c. Green ||31-32|| systemic back.
   d. Indigo ||44|| on #18.
   NOTE: Excessive exercise or any of several diseases may be causal. Do not run or jog hard on an empty urinary bladder.

- -

149. Albumin in the urine
   a. Lemon ||22|| systemic back.
   b. Magenta ||69|| on #18.
   NOTE: Severe exertion, a cold bath, poor diet, etc., may be causal.

- -

150. Hemoglobinuria, paroxysmal cold hemoglobinuria
   a. Lemon ||22|| systemic front.
   b. Magenta ||64-66-67|| systemic front and back.
   NOTE: Body warmth must be maintained at all times; even a cold drink can precipitate an attack. Syphilis may be associated.

- -

151. Pyuria, pyelitis, cystitis
       If condition focus is in front:
   a. Green ||32|| systemic front.
   b. Indigo ||44-47|| on #10-11.
       If condition focus is in back:
   c. Green ||32|| systemic back.
   d. Indigo ||45-47|| on #18-19.
   NOTE: In many cases, tonations may be required on front and back areas.

- -

152. Pneumaturia
   a. Green ||32|| on #10-11-18.
   b. Lemon ||22|| systemic front.
   c. Indigo ||44|| on #9-10 if with intestinal abscesses, leading to a fistula.
   NOTE: Often associated with vesico-enteric fistula.

- -

153. Lithuria
   a. Lemon ||22|| systemic front.
   b. Magenta ||69|| on #18.
       (Continued on next page)

NOTE: Drink water freely; increase intake of foods high in mineral salts. Avoid all meat, fish, coffee and tea.

- -

154. Oxaluria
   a. Lemon ‖22‖ systemic front.
   b. Yellow ‖18‖ on #6-7-8-9-10.
   c. Magenta ‖69‖ on #18.
   NOTE: Drink water freely. Avoid foods containing oxalic acid until condition improves.

- -

155. Indicanuria
   a. Lemon ‖22‖ systemic front.
   b. Magenta ‖69‖ on #18.
   NOTE: Diet may need improvement. Gallstones, wasting diseases, peritonitis, excess stomach acid, etc., may be involved and require attention.

- -

156. Cystinuria
   a. Lemon ‖22-27‖ systemic front.
   b. Magenta ‖69‖ on #18.
   NOTE: May require decrease of dietary protein and increase of foods with alkaline residue.

- -

157. Hydronephrosis
   a. Lemon ‖22‖ systemic back.
   b. Indigo ‖44‖ and Magenta ‖69‖ on #18.
   NOTE: The cause must be found promptly as it is often a mechanical obstruction which may require surgery or other intervention.

- -

158. Kidney stones (nephrolithiasis)
   a. Lemon ‖22‖ and Magenta ‖66-69‖ systemic back.
   NOTE: Drink water freely. Depending on location and size, stones may require removal.

- -

159. Addison's disease (adrenal tuberculosis or atrophy)
   a. Lemon ‖22‖ and Scarlet ‖75‖ systemic front and back (especially Scarlet on #18).
   b. Green ‖30‖ on #1.
   NOTE: Water and electrolyte balance may be seriously altered and require attention.

- -

160. Acute hemorrhagic adrenalitis
   a. Green ‖32‖ systemic back.
   b. Indigo ‖44‖ and Magenta ‖67‖ on #18.
   NOTE: May be associated with purpura, fevers, etc.

Color attribute number: ‖00‖. Tonation areas: #0-00.

161. **Adrenal cancer (see schedule #177, cancer)**
  a. Lemon ‖22‖ systemic back.
  b. Indigo ‖44‖ on #1

- -

162. **Adrenal overactivity, Cushing's syndrome (adrenal hypertrophy or hyperfunction)**
  a. Lemon ‖22‖ systemic back.
  b. Green ‖30‖ on #1.
  c. Purple ‖53‖ on #18.
  d. In hypertrophy, add Indigo ‖44‖ on #18.
  NOTE: Oat-cell lung cancer may be involved.

- -

163. **Adrenal underactivity (secondary adrenal insufficiency)**
  a. Lemon ‖22‖ systemic back.
  b. Green ‖30‖ on #1 if underlying cause is panhypopituitarism.
  c. Indigo ‖44‖ on #1-15 if brain tumor is present.
  d. Scarlet ‖70‖ on #18; Magenta ‖67‖ also may be useful.
  NOTE: Thyroid and reproductive functions may be affected.

- -

164. **Hemorrhoids (piles)**
  a. Lemon ‖22‖ systemic front and on #19.
  b. Indigo ‖44‖ on #19.
  NOTE: Constipation and its often attendant straining to begin a movement is a common cause; see Chapter five, part one, paragraph q. Diet probably needs improvement. Other diseases are sometimes involved.

- -

165. **Acute meningitis**
  a. Green ‖32‖ and Indigo ‖44-45-47‖ systemic back.
  b. Magenta ‖65‖ on #4-5, Purple ‖60‖ if fever is high.
  c. Scarlet ‖72‖ systemic front and back if circulatory collapse appears imminent.
  NOTE: Dehydration is common and must be treated promptly.

- -

166. **Chronic meningitis**
  a. Lemon ‖22‖ and Green ‖32‖ systemic back.
  NOTE: Tonate existing symptoms or as they develop.

- -

167. **Spinal hemorrhage (hematorachis, hematomyelia)**
  a. Turquoise ‖33‖ and Indigo ‖44‖ systemic back.
  b. If with paralysis, also tonate Motor nervous system schedule (#276) systemic back.

- -

168. **Spinal growths: glioma–tumor–gliomatosis–hydromyelus (see schedule #177, tumors)**
  a. Motor nervous system schedule (#276) systemic back.
  b. Indigo ‖44‖ on affected area.

169. Red neuralgia (erythromelalgia)
   a. Lemon ‖22‖ and Magenta ‖66‖ systemic front to include affected areas.
   b. Purple ‖54-55‖ on affected areas (or systemic front) may be tried during attacks in secondary types.
   c. Scarlet ‖70-71‖ systemic back to include affected areas may be tried during attacks in primary typcs.
   NOTE: Any use of tobacco products must be stopped. Elevate affected extremities during attacks.

- -

170. Varicose veins
   a. Lemon ‖22‖ and Magenta ‖66‖ systemic to include affected areas.
   b. Indigo ‖44‖ on affected areas.
   c. Scarlet ‖73‖ on the affected areas may be useful in some cases.

- -

171. Hardening of the arteries (arteriosclerosis)
   a. Lemon ‖22‖, Purple ‖55‖, and Magenta ‖66‖ systemic front.
   NOTE: If with high blood pressure, see schedule #277.

- -

172. Buerger's disease (thrombo-angiitis obliterans), phlebitis, thrombophlebitis
   a. Lemon ‖22‖, Purple ‖54-57‖, and Magenta ‖66‖ systemic front from #22.
   b. Scarlet ‖74‖ on #4-5 in obliterans.
   NOTE: Any use of tobacco products must be stopped. Elevate affected extremities during attacks.

- -

173. Reynaud's disease
   a. Magenta ‖66‖ systemic front to include affected areas.
   b. Motor nervous system schedule (#276) systemic front and back to include affected areas.
   c. During attacks, Orange ‖9‖, Purple ‖57‖, or Scarlet ‖73‖ may be tried on affected areas.
   NOTE: Any use of tobacco products must be stopped. Body warmth must be carefully maintained, and emotional stress avoided.

- -

174. Anemia (see #309 for sickle-cell anemia, #316 for pernicious anemia)
   a. Red ‖3‖ and Lemon ‖22‖ systemic front from #22.
   NOTE: Underlying cause can be parasites, poor diet, hemorrhage, acute fever, poisons, etc.

- -

175. Chlorosis
   a. Red ‖3‖ and Lemon ‖22‖ systemic front from #22.
   b. Magenta ‖65-68‖ on #4-5 and #10-11 (or systemic front).

Color attribute number: ‖00‖.   Tonation areas: #0-00.

176. Leukemia
    a. Red ‖3‖ and Lemon ‖22‖ systemic front from #22.
    b. Magenta ‖66‖ systemic front.
    c. Indigo ‖44‖ on hemorrhages if they occur.

- -

177. Cancer, tumors, growths; malignant or benign, (carcinoma, sarcoma, neoplasm)
    a. Lemon ‖22‖ systemic to include affected area.
    b. Indigo ‖44‖ on affected area. If the mass is interfering with organic functions, it may have to be removed. Indigo may not be able to shrink it beyond a certain point, depending on its fibrous content.
    c. Orange ‖15‖ on the affected area may assist in reducing the mass.
NOTE: A diet high in uncooked foods/juices should be used. As with all serious conditions, and especially so here, the sooner tonations are begun the better chances are for a favorable outcome.

- -

178. Hodgkin's disease (lymphadenoma) - see #177, cancer
    a. Lemon ‖22‖ and Indigo ‖44‖ systemic front.
    b. Orange ‖14‖ on affected areas if bone involvement occurs.
    c. Yellow ‖17‖ systemic to include affected lymph nodes.
NOTE: Complications may include anemia, fever, jaundice, edema, boils, etc. Alcoholic drinks may cause severe pains.

- -

179. Scurvy
    a. Lemon ‖22‖ and Indigo ‖44‖ systemic front.
NOTE: A diet with a much higher level of vitamin C is imperative. Tonate complications as they occur.

- -

180. Beri-beri
    If with fever:
    a. Turquoise ‖33‖ and Magenta ‖66‖ systemic front.
    If with little or no fever:
    b. Magenta ‖66‖ and Motor nervous system schedule (#276) systemic front and back.
NOTE: Diet must be improved, especially with foods high in vitamin B-1: wheat germ, food-grade yeast, sunflower seeds, soybeans, peanuts, etc.

- -

181. Rickets, osteomalacia
    a. Lemon ‖22-24‖ and Orange ‖14‖ systemic front and back from #22.
    b. Magenta ‖69‖ on #18.
    c. Indigo ‖41‖ on #3 if parathyroids are involved.
NOTE: Intake of vitamin D must be increased; an improved diet may be essential.

182. Gout
    a. Lemon ‖22‖ and Magenta ‖66‖ systemic front from #22.
    b. Scarlet ‖70‖ on #18.
NOTE: Diet usually requires considerable improvement. Avoid alcoholic drinks. Drink water freely. Tonate acute symptoms as they occur.

- -

183. Obesity
    a. Lemon ‖22‖ systemic front, and if with:
       b. Pituitary dysfunction – Green ‖30‖ on #1.
       c. Hypothyroidism   – Orange ‖7‖ systemic front.
       d. Gonadal insufficiency – Green ‖29-30‖ on #1, and
                                    Scarlet ‖78‖ on #10-11-18.
       e. Cerebral tumor   – Indigo ‖44‖ on #1-15.
       f. Excessive hunger   – Violet ‖50‖ on #8-9-10.
       g. Water retention   – Green ‖30‖ on #1, and
                                      Scarlet ‖70‖ on #18.
NOTE: Dietary and exercise habits usually need improvement. Several small meals a day may help (instead of the typical three large meals). Emotional factors may be involved.

- -

184. Dercum's disease (adiposis dolorosa)
    a. Lemon ‖22‖ and Orange ‖15‖ systemic front.
    b. Green ‖30‖ on #1.
    c. Violet ‖51‖ on painful skin areas.
    d. Scarlet ‖70‖ on #18 may tried if asthenia occurs.
    e. Magenta ‖64‖ systemic front if mental changes are noted.

- -

185. Boils (furuncles), carbuncles
    a. Lemon ‖22‖ systemic to include the affected area, and these Colors on the affected area:
    b. Orange ‖15‖ until suppuration begins and throbbing is felt, then
    c. Green ‖31-32‖ until pus stops draining, then
    d. Replace Lemon tonations with Turquoise ‖35-36‖ systemic, and a few tonations of Indigo ‖44‖ on the affected area.
NOTE: If disorder is a recurring problem, between attacks tonate Yellow ‖17‖ and Lemon ‖22‖ systemic front for several weeks. Diet probably needs improvement.

- -

186. Skin diseases
    Moist or weeping types:
    a. Turquoise ‖33-35‖ systemic to include affected area until signs of drying appear, then also tonate:
    b. Indigo ‖44‖ on affected area.
    (Continued on next page)

Color attribute number: ‖00‖. Tonation areas: #0-00.

Dry or scaly types:

c. Lemon ‖22‖ systemic to include affected area, and

d. Orange ‖15‖ on affected area until area erupts and exudes freely (becomes a weeping type), then

e. Continue as listed for weeping types (a. and b.)

NOTE: Do not use soap on affected area. Diet, allergies, or emotional stress may be involved in some cases.

- -

187. Skin hemorrhages (purpura)

a. Lemon ‖22‖ systemic to include affected area.

b. Indigo ‖44‖ and Magenta ‖66‖ on affected areas.

NOTE: Other diseases are often associated.

- -

188. Bleeding injury, hemorrhage

a. Indigo ‖44‖ on affected area until bleeding stops, then

b. Turquoise ‖33-35‖ systemic to include affected area, and

c. Green ‖32‖ and Magenta ‖66‖ on affected area.

NOTE: Stitches, taping, or a compression bandage may be necessary if injury is severe.

- -

189. Burns from fire or heat (infra-red burn)

a. Blue ‖39‖ and Indigo ‖44-47‖ on affected area until pain subsides and a crust or scab forms (an extended tonation is often useful, especially in cases with large involved areas), then

b. Turquoise ‖33-35‖ systemic to include affected area.

c. Green ‖31-32‖ on affected area.

d. Scarlet ‖70‖ on #18 if kidney functions falter.

e. Indigo ‖44-47‖ on affected area if exudation or pain continues.

- -

190. Burns from: x-rays – radiation – ultra-violet – Sunburn

When there is more than a little fever:

a. Blue ‖39‖ or Indigo ‖47‖ systemic to include affected area.

b. Red ‖5‖ on affected area, or systemic if needed (some cases respond to this Color alone).

With little or no fever:

c. Green ‖29-31‖ systemic to include affected area.

d. Red ‖5‖ on affected area, or systemic if needed.

e. Turquoise ‖35‖ on affected area if skin has been injured.

NOTE: Effects of radiation may not become apparent for some time—even several years.

- -

191. Tick itches, insect bites (parasitic arachnida). Dermatitis

a. Turquoise ‖33-35‖ and Blue ‖37‖ on affected areas.

NOTE: Tonate complications as they occur. For chronic dermatitis, use schedule #186.

192. Ainhum
- a. Lemon ‖**22**‖ systemic front to include affected area.
- b. Magenta ‖**66**‖ on affected area.

- -

193. Scleroderma
- a. Motor nervous system schedule (#276) systemic front.
- b. Green ‖**30**‖ on #1.
- c. Magenta ‖**66**‖ systemic to include affected areas (or Purple ‖**56**‖ if with high blood pressure).
- d. Magenta ‖**69**‖ on #18 (or Scarlet ‖**70**‖ if kidney failure appears imminent).

- -

194. Altitude sickness (anoxemia)
- a. Blue ‖**40**‖ systemic front.
- b. Orange ‖**6**‖ on #3-4-5-17.

NOTE: Supply additional oxygen; move to a lower altitude.

- -

195. Bends, diver's paralysis (caisson disease)
- a. Magenta ‖**66**‖ systemic to include affected area.
- b. If with paralysis, also tonate Motor nervous system schedule (#276) systemic back and include affected area.

NOTE: Recompression-decompression is usually essential. If bone necrosis is suspected tonate Orange ‖**14**‖ on affected area and Lemon ‖**22-24**‖ systemic to include affected area.

- -

196. Muscle stiffness, or cramps: writer's – swimmer's – stiff neck – etc.
- a. Orange ‖**9**‖ on affected area.

NOTE: Massage may be helpful. A change of bed pillows may help if neck stiffness persists.

- -

197. Loss of blood pressure, primary or secondary shock
- a. Scarlet ‖**72**‖ systemic front and back.

NOTE: The cause must be identified and treated.

- -

198. Acute alcoholism
- a. Blue ‖**39**‖ and Magenta ‖**64-66**‖ systemic front.
- b. Scarlet ‖**72**‖ systemic front and back if circulatory collapse appears imminent.
- c. Orange ‖**6**‖ on #3-4-5 if respiration rate is low; or systemic front for weakness, excessive perspiration, etc.

- -

199. Chronic alcoholism
- a. Motor nervous system schedule (#276) systemic front.
(Continued on next page)

Color attribute number: ‖**00**‖. Tonation areas: #0-00.

b. Magenta ‖**64-65-66**‖ systemic front.

c. Red ‖**2**‖ on #7-8.

NOTE: Alcohol intake must stopped as soon as possible. Tonate withdrawal symptoms as they appear. Emotional and dietary problems present in most cases must be resolved. (See schedule #323.)

----

200. Delirium tremens

a. Turquoise ‖**33**‖ and Magenta ‖**64-66**‖ systemic front.

b. Purple ‖**54-58-60**‖ on #1-2-3-4-5.

NOTE: After delirium is under control, tonations for alcoholism should be considered.

----

201. Drug addiction: heroin–morphine–opium etc.

a. Green ‖**29-30**‖ systemic front, and if with:

   b. Itching – Blue ‖**37**‖ on affected area.

   c. Poor digestion – Yellow ‖**18**‖ on #6-7-8-9-10.

   d. Restlessness – Violet ‖**51**‖ on #1 (or systemic front).

   e. Low heart rate – Magenta ‖**65-67**‖ on #4-5-18, or Scarlet ‖**70-74**‖ if rate is very low.

NOTE: Tonate symptoms as they appear. Emotional support may be essential for recovery. (See schedule #323.)

----

202. Lead poisoning

a. Lemon ‖**22**‖ systemic front.

NOTE: Tonate complications which may include: anemia, brain and heart disease, colitis, nephritis, neuritis, paralysis, etc. If poisoning is acute from eating lead paint, contact nearest poison control center, and begin first-aid measures if possible.

----

203. Arsenic poisoning

   Oral ingestion, acute:

a. Scarlet ‖**72**‖ systemic front and back if circulatory collapse appears imminent.

b. Stomach must be emptied as soon as possible, and washed with an antidote if available. If vomiting has begun, see schedule #105.

c. Indigo ‖**44-47**‖ on #6-8, but *only after* stomach has been properly emptied. **If electrolyte loss or dehydration is severe, immediate attention may be essential.**

d. Diarrhea will appear later, tonate Yellow ‖**19**‖ on #6-7-8-9-10 to hasten process. Enemas should be used to remove as much arsenic from the bowels as quickly as possible. Then

e. Tonate schedule #112, dysentery.

NOTE: Contact nearest poison control center, and begin first-aid if possible. Chronic poisoning:

f. Lemon ‖**22**‖ systemic front.

(Continued on next page)

g. Yellow ‖**18**‖ on #6-7-8-9-10.

h. Scarlet ‖**70**‖ on #18.

NOTE: Complications may include anemia, skin and liver diseases, paralysis, etc.

— —

204. Food poisoning

See schedule #105 for vomiting.

a. Green ‖**29-32**‖ systemic front.

b. Magenta ‖**65**‖ on #4-5.

NOTE: Contact nearest poison control center, and begin first-aid if possible.

— —

205. Sunstroke (asphyxial sunstroke)

a. Blue ‖**39**‖ systemic front.

b. Purple ‖**58-60**‖ on #4-5.

NOTE: Body temperature may rise to 107°F., and somewhat higher in extreme cases. A cold bath may be helpful, even essential; care must be taken to avoid over-cooling (hypothermia) or shock (circulatory collapse).

— —

206. Heat prostration (heat collapse or syncope)

a. Scarlet ‖**72**‖ systemic front and back.

NOTE: Body internal temperature is normal; circulatory failure causes skin to be cold and damp. Pulse is usually less than 100; blood pressure falls.

— —

207. Sprains

a. Indigo ‖**44-47**‖ on affected area (an extended tonation may be useful). After pain subsides:

b. Green ‖**31**‖ systemic to include affected area.

c. Orange ‖**15**‖ on affected area, and an occasional tonation of Indigo ‖**44**‖ on the same area.

— —

208. Bone fractures

a. Have fracture set or adjusted.

b. Orange ‖**14**‖ and Lemon ‖**24**‖ as close to the fracture as the cast will permit.

c. Blue ‖**37**‖ also may be tonated if itching develops.

— —

209. Acute bursitis or tendinitis. Tennis arm/elbow

a. Green ‖**31-32**‖ systemic to include affected area.

b. Blue ‖**39**‖ or Indigo ‖**44-45**‖ on affected area.

— —

210. Chronic bursitis or tendinitis

a. Lemon ‖**22**‖ systemic front to include affected area.

b. Orange ‖**15**‖ on affected area.

c. Blue ‖**39**‖ on affected area if still painful.

Color attribute number: ‖**00**‖. Tonation areas: #0-00.__

211. Reducible hernia, rupture

a. Lemon ‖22‖ systemic front.

b. Yellow ‖17‖ and Indigo ‖44‖ on affected area.

NOTE: Likely to be successful with children to five years of age; a supportive appliance (truss) may be necessary temporarily. May be helpful at any age but how effectively depends on individual circumstances.

---

212. Osteo-arthritis, rheumatoid arthritis

Acute condition:

a. Green ‖29-31-32‖ and Magenta ‖66‖ systemic to include affected areas.

b. Blue ‖39‖ or Indigo ‖45-47‖ on affected areas.

Chronic condition:

c. Lemon ‖22-24‖ and Magenta ‖66‖ systemic to include affected areas.

d. Turquoise ‖33‖ and/or Indigo ‖44-47‖ if with effusions or pain.

e. Orange ‖14‖ on areas of bone atrophy.

---

213. Paget's disease (osteitis deformans)

a. Lemon ‖22-24‖ and Magenta ‖66‖ systemic to include affected areas.

b. Orange ‖14‖ on affected areas.

c. Purple ‖54‖ may be tried on areas with bone aches.

d. Indigo ‖44‖ on #1-15 if with skull tumors.

---

214. Lobstein's disease (osteogenesis imperfecta)

a. Lemon ‖22-24‖ and Orange ‖14‖ systemic front from #22.

---

215. Marie's syndrome (hypertrophic pulmonary osteo-arthropy)

a. Lemon ‖22‖ and Magenta ‖66‖ systemic front from #22.

NOTE: Other diseases are usually involved or causative: tuberculosis, jaundice, nephritis, empyema, bronchiectasis, syphilis, etc.

---

216. Achondroplasia

a. Lemon ‖22-24‖ and Orange ‖14‖ systemic front and back from #22.

b. Green ‖30‖ on #1.

NOTE: By the time this condition is diagnosed, irreversible damage may have already occurred (united diaphyses, etc.), limiting the level of recovery possible.

---

217. Nerve inflammation (neuritis), nerve pain (neuralgia), sciatica

a. Turquoise ‖33‖ systemic to include affected area.

b. Indigo ‖47‖ on affected area.

c. If paralysis occurs, tonate Sensory or Motor nervous system schedule (#275 or #276) as required.

NOTE: May be associated with anemia, decayed teeth, bony spurs, latent nephritis, gout, etc.

218. Nerve tumors (neuromata) – see schedule #177, tumors
   a. Lemon ‖22‖ systemic to include affected area.
   b. Indigo ‖44‖ on affcctcd area.

_ _

219. Sleeping sickness (trypanosomiasis)
   a. Yellow ‖17-21‖ and Green ‖32‖ systemic front and on #16.
   b. Blue ‖39‖ systemic front if there is fever or convulsions.
   c. Magenta ‖65-66-69‖ on #4-5-18, and systemic to include any areas with edema.

_ _

220. Malaria
   a. Green ‖32‖ and Blue ‖39‖ systemic front.
   b. Purple ‖61‖ systemic front before and during paroxysms.
       During remissions, when fever is low:
   c. Yellow ‖17-21‖ and Lemon ‖22‖ systemic front.
   d. Red ‖2-3‖ systemic front from #22.
   e. Violet ‖48-52‖ on #6.

_ _

221. Psorospermiasis
   a. Yellow ‖21‖ and Green ‖31-32‖ systemic front.
   NOTE: Tonate complications as they occur.

_ _

222. Glanders, farcy
   a. Green ‖31-32‖ systemic front.
   b. Indigo ‖44‖ on affected area.

_ _

223. Actinomycosis
   a. Lemon ‖22‖ systemic front.
   b. Indigo ‖44‖ on affected area.
   c. Red ‖2‖ on #7-8 if liver is involved.
   NOTE: Tonate complications as they occur.

_ _

224. Typhoid or typhus fever
   a. Green ‖32‖ and Blue ‖39‖ systemic front.
   b. Magenta ‖65‖ on #4-5, or Purple ‖54-60‖ if
       with high fever or headache.
   NOTE: Complications are common and may be severe; tonate as they occur.
       For convalescence:
   c. Lemon ‖22-28‖ systemic front.
   d. After one week, also tonate Yellow ‖17‖ systemic front.
   e. Tonate appropriate stimulant Color on each organ
       which had been involved.
   f. Conclude with Turquoise ‖36‖ systemic front.

_ _

Color attribute number: ‖00‖.   Tonation areas: #0-00.

225. Chickenpox (varicella), measles (rubeola, rubella)
  a. Green ‖32‖ and Blue ‖37-39‖ systemic to include rash areas.
  b. Indigo ‖44‖ on hemorrhages if they occur.
  NOTE: Tonate complications if they occur.
      For convalescence:
  c. Lemon ‖28‖ systemic to include areas which
      had a rash, followed by Yellow ‖17‖.
  d. Conclude with Turquoise ‖35-36‖ systemic to
      include areas which had a rash.

- -

226. Relapsing or intermittent fevers
      When there is fever:
  a. Green ‖32‖, Blue ‖39‖, and Purple ‖61‖ systemic front.
  b. Magenta ‖65‖ on #4-5.
      When there is little or no fever:
  c. Lemon ‖22‖ and Yellow ‖17‖ systemic front.
  d. Magenta ‖65‖ on #4-5.
  e. When fever no longer recurs, conclude with Turquoise systemic front.

- -

227. Smallpox (variola)
  a. Green ‖32‖ and Blue ‖39‖ systemic to include rash areas.
  b. Magenta ‖65‖ on #4-5.
  c. Indigo ‖44‖ on hemorrhages if they occur.
      For convalescence:
  d. Lemon ‖22‖ systemic to include areas which
      had a rash, followed by Yellow ‖17‖.
  e. Magenta ‖66‖ on areas which had a hemorrhage.
  f. Conclude with Turquoise ‖35-36‖ systemic to
      include areas which had a rash.

- -

228. Mumps (parotitis)
  a. Green ‖32‖ and Blue ‖39‖ systemic front (and back if
      spine is involved).
      For convalescence:
  b. Lemon ‖22-28‖ systemic front (and back if
      with spine involvement), followed by Yellow ‖17‖.
  c. Conclude with Turquoise ‖36‖ systemic front.
  NOTE: Be sure area #11 is included in front tonations.

- -

229. Scarlet fever
  a. Green ‖32‖ and Blue ‖39‖ systemic to include rash areas.
  b. Magenta ‖65‖ on #4-5, or Purple ‖60‖ if with high fever.
  c. Indigo ‖44‖ on hemorrhages if they occur.
      (Continued on next page)

For convalescence:

d. Lemon ‖22-28‖ systemic to include areas which had a rash, followed by Yellow ‖17‖.

e. Conclude with Turquoise ‖35-36‖ systemic to include areas which had a rash.

- -

230. Whooping cough (pertussis)

Catarrhal stage, or when there is fever:

a. Green ‖32‖ and Blue ‖39‖ systemic front.

b. Magenta ‖65-66‖ on #1-2-3-4-5.

c. Indigo ‖44-47‖ on #1-2 for pain and/or hemorrhage.

Paroxysmal stage, or when there is little or no fever:

d. Lemon ‖23‖ systemic front.

e. Orange ‖6-15‖ on #2-3-4-5 may aid in loosening phlegm.

f. Magenta ‖65-66‖ on #1-2-3-4-5.

For convalescence:

g. Lemon ‖22-23‖ systemic front, and after one week Yellow ‖17‖ also. Conclude with Turquoise ‖36‖ systemic front.

- -

231. Flu (influenza, grippe)

a. Green ‖32‖ and Blue ‖39‖ systemic front.

b. Magenta ‖65-66‖ on #4-5.

c. Purple ‖54-60-63‖ on #1-2-3-4-5 may be tonated for headache, fever, dry cough (see Purple ‖63‖ attribute).

NOTE: At first sign of onset tonate Scarlet ‖74‖ once on #1-2-3-4-5; take deep breaths. Flu can have varied and sometimes severe complications; tonate accordingly.

- -

232. Diphtheria

a. Green ‖32‖ and Blue ‖39‖ systemic front.

b. Magenta ‖65‖ on #4-5, or Purple ‖60‖ if fever is high.

c. Magenta ‖69‖ on #18, or Scarlet ‖70‖ if urine suppression occurs.

d. Indigo ‖44‖ on membranes (areas #1-2-3), and hemorrhages if they occur.

NOTE: Complications are common, varied, and may be severe.

For convalescence:

e. Lemon ‖22-28‖ systemic front, followed by Yellow ‖17‖.

f. If nerve damage or paralysis has occurred, tonate one of the Nervous system schedules (#275 or #276).

g. Magenta ‖65‖ on #4-5.

h. Conclude with Turquoise ‖36‖ systemic front.

Color attribute number: ‖00‖.   Tonation areas: #0-00.

233. Rocky Mountain spotted fever, tick fever (cerebrospinal fever)
   a. Green ||32|| and Indigo ||44-47|| systemic front and back.
   b. Magenta ||65|| on #4-5, or Purple ||60-63|| if with high fever or dry cough (see attribute ||63||).
   c. Blue ||39|| systemic front if with high fever.
   NOTE: Complications are common, varied, and may be severe.
      For convalescence:
   d. Sensory nervous system schedule (#275) systemic back.
   e. Tonate appropriate stimulant Color on each organ which had been involved.
   f. Conclude with Turquoise ||36|| systemic front and back.

- -

234. Breakbone fever (dengue)
   a. Green ||32|| and Blue ||39|| systemic front.
   b. Purple ||54-60|| systemic front to include extremities when with high fever and pain, Magenta ||66|| at other times.
   c. Scarlet ||71-72|| systemic front and back if circulatory collapse (fever shock syndrome) appears imminent.
   d. Indigo ||44-47|| systemic front and on hemorrhages.
      For convalescence:
   e. Lemon ||22-28|| systemic to include rash areas (a few cases do not have a rash).
   f. After one week add Yellow ||17|| systemic front.
   g. Continue Lemon and Yellow for three weeks after all obvious symptoms disappear.
   h. Conclude with Turquoise ||36|| systemic front.

- -

235. Rheumatic fever
   a. Green ||32|| and Indigo ||44-45-47|| systemic to include affected joints.
   b. Magenta ||65|| on #4-5-18.
   c. Purple ||63|| on #4-5 if dry cough occurs (see attribute ||63||).
   d. Scarlet ||70|| on #18 if kidney function falters or edema occurs.
      For convalescence:
   e. Lemon ||22-28|| systemic front, and after one week add Yellow ||17||.
   f. Magenta ||65|| on #4-5.
   g. Continue Yellow, Lemon, Magenta, for several months after all symptoms have disappeared.
   h. Conclude with Turquoise ||36|| systemic front.

- -

236. Cholera asiatica, cholera nostras
      Preliminary stage:
   a. Green ||32|| systemic front.
   b. Indigo ||44-47|| on #6-7-8-9-10.

(Continued on next page)

If collapse stage occurs:

c. Scarlet ‖**72**‖ systemic front and back.

d. Resume a. and b. tonations after danger of collapse eases.
   Reaction stage, or convalescence:

e. Lemon ‖**22-28**‖ systemic front, and Yellow ‖**17**‖ after one week.

f. Magenta ‖**65**‖ on 34-5.

g. Orange ‖**9**‖ on areas with muscle cramps.

h. Conclude with Turquoise ‖**36**‖ systemic front.

NOTE: **If electrolyte loss or dehydration is severe, immediate attention may be essential.**

- -

237. Yellow fever

a. Green ‖**32**‖ , Blue ‖**39**‖ , and Magenta ‖**66**‖ systemic front.

b. Indigo ‖**44-45**‖ on #6-8, and on hemorrhages.

c. Scarlet ‖**67**‖ on #18.

d. Red ‖**2**‖ on #7-8.
   For convalescence:

e. Lemon ‖**22**‖ systemic front, and Yellow ‖**17**‖ after one week.

f. Magenta ‖**65**‖ on #4-5.

g. Red ‖**2**‖ on #7-8.

h. Conclude with Turquoise ‖**36**‖ systemic front.

NOTE: **If electrolyte loss or dehydration is severe, immediate attention may be essential..**

- -

238. Bubonic plague, septicemic plague

a. Green ‖**32**‖ and Magenta ‖**66**‖ systemic front.

b. Blue ‖**39**‖ systemic front, or Indigo ‖**44**‖ if hemorrhages occur.

c. Purple ‖**60**‖ on #4-5 (or systemic) when fever is high.

d. Scarlet ‖**72**‖ systemic front and back if circulatory
   collapse appears imminent.
   For convalescence:

e. Lemon ‖**22-28**‖ systemic front, and Yellow ‖**17**‖ after one week.

f. Magenta ‖**66**‖ systemic front.

g. Conclude with Turquoise ‖**36**‖ systemic front.

- -

239. Malta fever (brucellosis)

When there is fever:

a. Green ‖**32**‖ and Blue ‖**39**‖ systemic front.

b. Purple ‖**60**‖ on #4-5 (or systemic) if with high fever.

c. Yellow ‖**18**‖ on #8-9-10 if constipation occurs.
   With little or no fever:

d. Yellow ‖**17**‖ and Lemon ‖**22-28**‖ systemic front.

e. See schedule #226 if fever becomes recurrent.

Color attribute number: ‖**00**‖. Tonation areas: #0-00.

240. Miliary fever
 a. Green ‖32‖ and Magenta ‖66‖ systemic front.
 b. Blue ‖39‖ systemic front, or Indigo ‖44‖ if hemorrhages occur.
 c. Purple ‖60‖ on #4-5 (or systemic) if with high fever.
  For convalescence:
 d. Lemon ‖22-28‖ systemic to include areas with vesicles, and
  Yellow ‖17‖ after a few days.
 e. Conclude with Turquoise ‖35-36‖ systemic to include areas which had
  vesicles.

- -

241. Canker sores (aphthous stomatitis)
 a. Green ‖32‖ systemic front and in mouth.
 b. Blue ‖39‖ on #1 and in mouth, systemic front if with fever.
 c. Indigo ‖47‖ or Violet ‖51‖ may be tried on painful sores.
NOTE: If sores tend to recur, between attacks tonate Lemon ‖22‖ and
Yellow ‖17‖ systemic front from #22.

- -

242. Leprosy
 a. Lemon ‖22‖ and Green ‖32‖ systemic to include areas with lesions.
 b. Blue ‖39‖ on areas of neuritis, or systemic front (instead of Lemon)
  when there is fever.
 c. If with paralysis, Motor nervous system schedule (#276) systemic to
  include those areas.
NOTE: Tonate any organ which becomes involved (see Color attributes).

- -

243. Ephemeral fever, febricula
See schedule #315, Unexplained fever.

- -

244. Milk sickness, trembles
 a. Green ‖32‖ and Indigo ‖45-47‖ systemic front.
 b. Yellow ‖18-19‖ on #8-9-10 if constipated (see schedule #109).

- -

245. Infectious mononucleosis, glandular fever
 a. Green ‖32‖ and Blue ‖39‖ systemic front.
 b. Magenta ‖65-67‖ on #4-5-18, or Purple ‖60‖ on #4-5 (or systemic)
  when fever is high.
 c. Yellow ‖17‖ on areas of lymphatic involvement.
NOTE: Various organs may be affected and require attention.
  For convalescence:
 d. Lemon ‖22-28‖ systemic front for one week, then
 e. Lemon ‖22-28‖ and Yellow ‖17‖ systemic to include
  lymphatics which were affected; tonate for at least one
  month (glandular involvement may not appear for three weeks).
 f. Conclude with Turquoise ‖36‖ systemic front.

246. Anthrax
   a. Yellow ‖**17**‖ and Green ‖**32**‖ systemic front.
   b. Blue ‖**39**‖ systemic front, or Indigo ‖**44**‖ if with
       effusions or hemorrhages.
   c. Magenta ‖**65**‖ on #4-5, or if edema occurs:
   d. Magenta ‖**65-66**‖ systemic front and Scarlet ‖**70**‖ on #18.
   e. Scarlet ‖**72**‖ systemic front and back if
       circulatory collapse appears imminent.
   NOTE: Complications may be varied and severe. Pulmonary anthrax is
   often fatal; use extreme care.

- -

247. Rabies, hydrophobia
       Premonitory stage:
   a. Green ‖**32**‖ systemic front and back.
   b. Blue ‖**39**‖ systemic front.
   c. Yellow ‖**16-17**‖ systemic back.
       Excitement stage:
   d. Yellow ‖**16-17**‖ systemic back (keep Color from
       shining on front areas).
   e. Magenta ‖**65-66**‖ on #1-2-3-4-5.
   f. Violet ‖**51-52**‖ systemic front.
       Paralytic stage:
   g. Scarlet ‖**71**‖ systemic front and back.
   NOTE: Condition is extremely serious, usually fatal.

- -

248. Lockjaw (tetanus)
   a. Green ‖**32**‖ and Purple ‖**54-60**‖ systemic to include injury area.
   b. Blue ‖**39**‖ systemic front.
   c. Magenta ‖**65**‖ on #4-5.
   d. Orange ‖**9**‖ and/or Yellow ‖**16**‖ may be
       tried systemic back and on areas with spasms.
       For convalescence:
   e. Magenta ‖**66**‖ and Motor nervous system schedule (#276) systemic to
       include injury site.

- -

249. Septicemia
   a. Green ‖**32**‖ systemic front.
   b. Blue ‖**39**‖ systemic front, or Indigo ‖**44**‖ if with hemorrhages.
   c. Magenta ‖**65**‖ on #4-5, or Purple ‖**60**‖ if with high fever.
   d. Scarlet ‖**72**‖ systemic front and back if septic shock occurs.
   e. Yellow ‖**17**‖ and Lemon ‖**22-28**‖ systemic front and
       back may be required for several weeks. If fever
       recurs, see schedule #315, Unexplained fever.

Color attribute number: ‖**00**‖. Tonation areas: #0-00.

250. Erysipelas
   a. Green ‖32‖ systemic front.
   b. Magenta ‖66‖ systemic front, or Purple ‖54-60‖ if fever is high.
   c. Magenta ‖67-68‖ on #18.
   d. Blue ‖39‖ systemic front, or see schedule #296 if suppuration occurs.
   NOTE: See schedule #311 if lymphedema occurs.

- -

251. Pyemia, septicopyemia
   a. Green ‖32‖ and Indigo ‖44-45‖ systemic front.
   b. Magenta ‖65‖ on #4-5, or Purple ‖60‖ if with high fever (systemic may be tonated).

- -

252, 253. Locomotor ataxia (tabes dorsalis), general paresis
   a. Green ‖29-32‖ on #1, and systemic front.
   b. Sensory nervous system schedule (#275) systemic back, and on #1 if eyes are involved.
   c. Magenta ‖64-66‖ systemic front.
   NOTE: Syphilis is the cause of these disorders, and may involve various organs.

- -

254. Shingles (herpes zoster)
   Acute stage (vesicles):
   a. Green ‖32‖ and Indigo ‖44-45-47‖ systemic back, and on
      any affected areas.
      Chronic stage:
   b. Motor nervous system schedule (#276) systemic back, and on
      affected areas.
   c. Violet ‖51‖ on painful areas.
   NOTE: Take great care to keep eyes clean; also tonate on #1 if eyes are involved.

- -

255. Little's disease (tetraplegia spastica)
   Early stage (hemorrhage, breathing difficulty):
   a. Indigo ‖44‖ on #1-15-16.
   b. Orange ‖6‖ on #3-4-5-17.
   As soon as condition allows, begin schedule for later stage (do not wait for symptoms to appear–spasm, paralysis, etc.):
   c. Sensory nervous system schedule (#275) systemic back.

- -

256. Polio (acute anterior poliomyelitis), multiple sclerosis, progressive bulbar paralysis. primary lateral sclerosis, diffuse sclerosis, degenerative myelitis, infantile hemiplegia (palsy), muscular dystrophy, Werdnig-Hoffman muscular atrophy, etc.
   a. Green ‖31-32‖ systemic to include affected areas.
   b. Blue ‖39‖ systemic front when there is fever.
      (Continued on next page)

    c. Motor nervous system schedule (#276) systemic front and back to include affected areas.

    d. Scarlet ‖71‖ systemic to include affected areas, in muscular atrophy or dystrophy.

NOTE: An adequate natural (unrefined) diet with many raw foods is of utmost importance. Eliminate refined sugar, white flour, and other typical "junk-foods" from the diet. A regimen of physical therapy, massage, exercise, etc., should be implemented when appropriate.

– –

257. Tay-Sachs' disease (amaurotic family idiocy)

    a. Green ‖29-30-31‖ systemic front and back.

    b. Sensory nervous system schedule (#275) systemic front and back.

NOTE: Condition is hereditary, considered incurable and fatal, but these Colors may be tried. See note in schedule #256.

– –

258. Thomsen's disease (myotonia congenita)

    a. Green ‖29-31‖ and Purple ‖54‖ systemic front.

    b. Motor nervous system schedule (#276) systemic to include affected areas. See note in schedule #256.

– –

259. Suppurative myositis

See schedule #296, abscess.

– –

260. Myasthenia gravis

    a. Motor nervous system schedule (#276) systemic front and back.

    b. Indigo ‖44‖ on #4-5 (thymus) if with thymoma.

    c. Scarlet ‖71‖ systemic front and back.

– –

261. Oppenheim's disease (amyotonia congenita)

Tonate (and see Note) as listed in schedule #256.

– –

262. Parkinson's disease (paralysis agitans, shaking palsy)

    a. Motor nervous system schedule (#276) on #1-15.

NOTE: Other disorders may be involved.

– –

263. Sydenham's chorea (acute chorea)

    a. Turquoise ‖33‖ and Violet ‖49‖ systemic front.

    b. Magenta ‖65‖ on #4-5, or Purple ‖60‖ if with high fever.

    c. If paralysis persists, tonate Motor nervous system schedule (#276) systemic back.

Color attribute number: ‖00‖.   Tonation areas: #0-00.

264. Habit spasms or tics
   a. Violet ‖**49-51**‖ systemic front.
   b. Magenta ‖**64**‖ on #1.
   c. Orange ‖**9**‖ may be tried on affected areas.

- -

265. Infantile convulsions
   a. Blue ‖**39**‖ systemic front.
   NOTE: Many irritations and infections may be associated or causal: teething, otitis, digestive upset, phimosis, etc. Convulsions also may signal the onset of serious diseases: brain tumors, encephalitis, meningitis, scarlet fever, etc. If cause is not determined, tonate:
   b. Green ‖**29-32**‖ and Blue ‖**39-40**‖ systemic front until there are no episodes for a week, then
   c. Lemon ‖**22**‖ systemic front followed by Yellow ‖**17**‖.

- -

266. Epilepsy
   a. Purple systemic front.
   b. Motor nervous system schedule (#276) on #1-15.
   c. Indigo ‖**44**‖ on #1-15 if with cerebral hemorrhage, tumor or abscess.
   NOTE: There are seizures caused by infections, injuries, toxic agents, brain disorders, etc., which may be confused with epileptic episodes.

- -

267. Hemophilia
   a. Lemon ‖**22**‖ and Magenta ‖**64-66**‖ systemic front from #22.
   b. Indigo ‖**44**‖ on areas with hemorrhages.
   c. Red ‖**2-3**‖ on #7-8.
   NOTE: This is considered to be an incurable genetic disorder, but it may be worth trying tonations for a few months.

- -

268. Chronic drowsiness
   a. Lemon ‖**22**‖ systemic front.
   b. Magenta ‖**64-66**‖ systemic front and back, and Scarlet ‖**71**‖ also may be tried if blood pressure is not too high.
   NOTE: Dietary and emotional factors may be involved.

- -

269. Uncontrollable overactivity (hyperkinesis)
   Depending on causative factors, either of these (or a combination) may be effective:
   a. Turquoise ‖**33-34**‖ and Violet ‖**49-51**‖ systemic front.
   b. Lemon ‖**22-25**‖ and Orange ‖**9-15**‖ systemic front.
   NOTE: Avoid exposure to fluorescent lighting. Do not eat foods containing artificial colors or flavors, or preservatives; read the labels on prepared foods and buy or discard accordingly.

270. Functional overactivity
   a. Green ‖**29-30**‖ on #1, or systemic front.
   b. Violet ‖**49-51**‖ systemic front.
   NOTE: If a particular organ is overactive, see the Table of Color Attributes for its stimulant Color and then tonate the OPPOSITE Color.

- -

271. Hatred, human repugnance
   a. Green ‖**29**‖ on #1, or systemic front.
   b. Magenta ‖**64**‖ systemic front. (See schedule #323.)

- -

272. Melancholia
   a. Lemon ‖**22**‖ and Scarlet ‖**71**‖ systemic front.
   b. Yellow ‖**20**‖ on #6-7. (See schedule #323.)

- -

273. Hysteria
   a. Blue ‖**39-40**‖ and Magenta ‖**64**‖ systemic front.
   b. Green ‖**29-30**‖ on #1, or systemic front.
   c. Scarlet ‖**77**‖ on #10-11.
   NOTE: Mental attitude is very important; suggestotherapy, etc., may be useful. See schedule #323.

- -

274. Palliation of pain
   a. Indigo ‖**44**‖, Violet ‖**49-51**‖, or Purple ‖**54**‖ may
       be tried on affected area.
   b. Systemic tonations to include the affected area may be more effective.
   NOTE: For recurrent pains, the cause should be found and corrected.

- -

275. Sensory nervous system schedule. Macular degeneration.
   This schedule is used in disorders with loss or impairment of any of the senses. Colors are tonated systemic in most cases (Lemon ‖**22**‖ should be tonated systemic in all cases). Individual condition listings indicate whether to tonate front or back areas.
   a. Lemon ‖**22**‖ and Yellow ‖**16-17**‖ for two weeks, then
   b. Lemon ‖**22**‖ and Orange ‖**15**‖ for four weeks, then
   c. Lemon ‖**22**‖ and Red ‖**1**‖ for six weeks.
   d. For macular degeneration also tonate Magenta ‖**66**‖ on #1-2-3-4-5;
       Indigo ‖**44**‖ on #1 if with hemorrhages.
   NOTE: Repeat the schedule until desired results are attained. Nerve repair is often a slow process; be patient. Macular degeneration is associated with other disorders which must be controlled.

276. Motor nervous system schedule

This schedule is used in disorders with loss or impairment of movement abilities. Colors are tonated systemic in most cases (Lemon ‖22‖ should be tonated systemic in all cases). Individual condition listings indicate whether to tonate front or back areas.

a. Lemon ‖22‖ and Yellow ‖16-17‖ for two weeks, then

b. Lemon ‖22‖ and Orange ‖15‖ for four weeks.

NOTE: Repeat the schedule until desired results are attained. Nerve repair is often a slow process; be patient.

- -

277. High blood pressure (hypertension), pheochromocytoma

a. Lemon ‖22‖ and Purple ‖56‖ systemic front and
back (tonating systemic from #22 is more effective in
some cases and may be essential).

b. Magenta ‖65-67‖ on #4-5-18.

c. Indigo ‖44‖ systemic front and back if with tumors in
the chromaffin system.

d. Indigo ‖44‖ on #18 if with tumors in kidneys or adrenals.

NOTE: Persistent blood pressure above 140/90-mmhg (when at rest) in adults (much lower in children) may be termed high blood pressure. Several factors may be involved and require attention: heart/kidney/adrenal disorders, endocrine system disturbance, oral contraceptives, obesity, etc. Tonate this schedule until cause is determined.

- -

278. Low blood pressure (hypotension)

a. Lemon ‖22‖ and Scarlet ‖72‖ systemic front and
back (tonating systemic from #22 is more effective in
some cases and may be essential).

b. Magenta ‖65-67‖ on #4-5-18.

NOTE: Persistent systolic blood pressure below 110-mmhg in adults may be termed low blood pressure. Several factors may be involved and require attention: heart or circulatory dysfunction, hemorrhage, anemia, infections, severe diarrhea, neurologic lesions, etc. Tonate this schedule until cause is determined.

- -

279. Menopausal complaints

a. Green ‖29-30‖ and Magenta ‖64-66-67‖ systemic front and on #18.

NOTE: Emotional state must be considered. Also tonate specific symptoms which may occur: itching–Blue ‖37‖, poor digestion–Yellow ‖18‖, etc. DuoChrome (Chapter 13, using Green-Magenta) may be helpful.

- -

280. Carrier

a. Lemon ‖22‖ and Yellow ‖17‖ systemic front and back.

NOTE: A "carrier" is a person who harbors specific organisms while exhibiting no symptoms from their presence, but transmission is possible in diverse ways to other persons who may develop the usual disease of the

(Continued on next page)

organism. A test may be available to check on progress; if it is reliable, tonate until it is negative.

- -

281. Allergies
a. Lemon ‖22‖ systemic front and back from #22, and
b. Yellow ‖17‖ systemic front for two weeks, then
c. Orange ‖15‖ systemic front (instead of Yellow) for two weeks.
NOTE: Also tonate symptoms as they occur. Repeat schedule as needed.

- -

282. Gangrene, blood clots, intermittent claudication
a. Lemon ‖22‖ and Magenta ‖64-66‖ systemic front to
include affected areas.
b. Scarlet ‖74‖ on #4-5 if blood pressure is not too high.
NOTE: Exercise carefully to increase circulation. Any use of tobacco must be stopped. See schedule #82 for lung gangrene.

- -

283. Peyronie's disease (penile induration)
a. Lemon ‖22‖ systemic front.
b. Orange ‖15‖ on #11 may aid in dissolving the fibrous chordee.

- -

284. Shivering, chills
Shivering is an indication that the body requires a higher internal temperature – try Scarlet ‖72‖ on #1-2-3-4-5-18 or systemic. Chills may be felt at the onset of a fever or other problem; try Purple ‖63‖ on #1-2-3-4-5. If onset is felt without chills, see note in schedule #231, and may be followed with schedule #315.

- -

285. Tinnitus
a. Sensory nervous system schedule (#275) on #1 if for a nerve problem.
NOTE: Other conditions causing ear noises may be: obstructing ear-wax, certain drugs, infections, tumors, alcohol, injuries, syphilis, etc.

- -

286. Edema, anasarca, dropsy
a. Lemon ‖22‖ systemic front and back.
b. Magenta ‖65‖ on #4-5 or systemic front.
c. Scarlet ‖70‖ on #18.
NOTE: Heart, liver, or kidney disease may be present.

- -

287. Slipped spinal disk (herniated nucleus pulposus)
a. Lemon ‖22‖ systemic back.
b. Indigo ‖44‖ on affected area.

Color attribute number: ‖00‖. Tonation areas: #0-00.

288. Cystic fibrosis (mucoviscidosis)
   a. Lemon ‖22‖ systemic front from #22, and on #18 (pancreas).
   b. Yellow ‖18‖ on #6-7-8-9-10-18-19.
   c. Try Orange ‖15‖ on areas with viscid secretions, such as #4-5-17.
   d. Try Indigo ‖44‖ on areas with normal but excessive secretions.

— —

289. Immune deficiency - acquired or congenital
   a. Red ‖3‖ and Lemon ‖22-26‖ systemic front from #22.
   b. Yellow ‖17‖ systemic front.
   c. Violet ‖48‖ on #6.
   NOTE: Tonations may have limited effect if the spleen or thymus is absent (congenital or otherwise), but these Colors may be tried as well as tonations for symptoms.

— —

290. Lupus (systemic lupus erythematosus)
   a. Lemon ‖22‖ systemic front from #22.
   b. Violet ‖48‖ on #6.
   c. Blue ‖39‖ systemic to include involved joints or skin areas.
   d. Magenta ‖65-69‖ on #4-5-18.
   e. Indigo ‖44‖ and Magenta ‖66‖ on skin hemorrhages.
   NOTE: This serious and complex disease may involve any or several organs, requiring appropriate Colors on affected areas.

— —

291. Osteoporosis
   a. Orange ‖14‖ and Lemon ‖22-24‖ systemic front from #22, and systemic back if spine is involved.
   b. Magenta ‖65-69‖ on #4-5-18.
   c. Yellow ‖18‖ on #6-7-8-9-10.
   d. Indigo ‖41‖ on #3 (parathyroid) may be tried.
   NOTE: The cause of osteoporosis is not completely understood. Calcium and/or vitamin D deficiency or absorption may be factors. Changes in calcitrol and sex-hormone production (especially after menopause) have been implicated. Other medical problems may cause secondary osteoporosis, and require attention.

— —

292. Hemorrhagic stroke (cerebro-vascular hemorrhagic accident)
   As soon as condition becomes apparent:
   a. Purple ‖56‖ on #1-2-3-4-5.
   b. Indigo ‖44‖ on #1-15.
   When condition has stabilized:
   c. Lemon ‖22‖ systemic front.
   d. Magenta ‖66‖ on #1-2-3-4-5.
   e. Indigo ‖44‖ on #1-15 if even slight hemorrhage continues.
   f. Motor nervous system schedule (#276) if paralysis occurs.
   NOTE: Most hemorrhagic strokes are caused by an aneurism, arterial disease and/or high blood pressure; tonate accordingly.

293. Anorexia nervosa
   a. Green ‖**28**‖ and Magenta ‖**64**‖ systemic front.
   b. Yellow ‖**19**‖ on #6-7.
   NOTE: Emotional circumstances are extremely important in this disorder. Tonate symptoms as they occur. (See schedule #323.)

294. Pinworms (enterobiasis)
   a. Yellow ‖**21**‖ on #6-7-8-9-10.
   b. Blue ‖**37**‖ on #19 may help for local (anal) itching.
   NOTE: Reinfestation is difficult to avoid as pinworm eggs can live for three weeks in upholstery, clothes, etc. The entire family may need tonations. Keep fingers away from mouth.

295. Sinus inflammation (sinusitis)
   a. Green ‖**32**‖ systemic front, or Lemon ‖**22**‖ if condition is chronic.
   b. Blue ‖**39**‖ on #1.
   NOTE: Abscessed teeth may need attention.

296. Abscess
   a. Green ‖**32**‖ systemic front.
   b. Indigo ‖**44-45-47**‖ on affected area.
   c. Orange ‖**15**‖ and Yellow ‖**17**‖ on affected area may help the abscess drain if it is in an area where it can break through the skin.
   d. Magenta ‖**65**‖ on #4-5, or Purple ‖**60**‖ if fever is high.
   e. Blue ‖**39**‖ systemic front if fever is high.
      If abscess has drained through the skin and healing has begun:
   f. Turquoise ‖**35**‖ systemic to include affected area.
   g. Indigo ‖**44**‖ on affected area.
   NOTE: Schedules for some abscesses may be found under appropriate headings. If encapsulation occurs, aspiration or removal may be necessary.

297. Bacteremia
   a. Green ‖**32**‖ and Blue ‖**39**‖ systemic front.
   b. Magenta ‖**65**‖ on #4-5, or Purple ‖**60-61**‖ if fever is high or recurring.
   NOTE: Blood-electrolyte imbalance, multiple abscesses, shock, kidney failure, or other life-threatening circumstances may develop.

298. Cat-scratch disease (benign lymphoreticulosis)
   a. Green ‖**32**‖ and Blue ‖**39**‖ systemic front to include affected lymph nodes.
   b. Yellow ‖**17**‖ on affected lymph nodes.
   c. Magenta ‖**65**‖ on #4-5.
   d. If draining fistulas form, see schedule #314–discharges.

Color attribute number: ‖**00**‖. Tonation areas: #0-00.__

299. Alzheimer's disease, senile dementia
  a. Lemon ‖22-25‖ systemic front.
  b. Magenta ‖65-66-67‖ on #1-2-3-4-5-18.
  c. Sensory nervous system schedule (#275) on #1.

NOTE: Loss of brain tissue is considered irreversible but it is possible for development of this condition to be slowed or halted. Other problems causing dementia can be alcoholism, tumors, syphilis, inflammations, vitamin deficiencies (poor diet), etc. Up to 30 times the usual amount of aluminum is often found in the brains of those with Alzheimer's disease but it is not known whether this is a cause or an effect. It would seem prudent to avoid unnecessary ingestion of aluminum, such as from cooking utensils, some bakery and leavening agents, and many anti-perspirants. Tonate symptoms as they occur. Physical and mental exercise may slow progress of this condition, according to recent research.

- -

300. Retinitis pigmentosa
  a. Sensory nervous system schedule (#275) on #1.
  b. Magenta ‖66‖ on #1-2-3-4-5.

- -

301. Congenital adrenal hyperplasia
  a. Lemon ‖22‖ systemic back.
  b. Magenta ‖67‖ on #18. Indigo ‖44‖ and Purple ‖53‖ may be tried.

- -

302. Athletic heart syndrome
  a. Green ‖29‖ and Magenta ‖65-66‖ systemic front.
  NOTE: The heart normally enlarges and slows in response to continued additional work load placed upon it but as the heart rate decreases, the ratio should remain normal. If arrhythmias develop, see schedule #71.

- -

303. Black eye, bruises
  a. Indigo ‖44-47‖ on affected area as soon as possible to limit swelling and pain (an extended tonation may be useful).
    After pain subsides:
  b. Orange ‖15‖ and Lemon ‖22‖ on affected area.

- -

304. Inflammation
  This schedule may be used for any inflammation not specifically listed.
  a. Green ‖29-32‖ and Blue ‖39‖ systemic to include affected area.
  b. Magenta ‖65‖ on #4-5, or Purple ‖58-60‖ if pulse rate is too fast or fever is high.
  c. Magenta ‖67‖ on #18.
  d. If fever persists, try Yellow ‖17‖ systemic to include affected area.

- -

305. Cough – productive of phlegm
  If with little or no fever:
  a. Lemon ‖22‖ systemic front and on #17.
  b. If condition is chronic, see Color schedule #81.
    (Continued on next page)

If there is fever:

c. Green ‖32‖ systemic front.

d. Magenta ‖65‖ on #4-5, or Purple ‖60‖ if fever is high.

e. Blue ‖39‖ on #1-2-3-4-5-17, or systemic front and on #17 if fever is high.

f. When fever drops, resume instruction a. or b.

NOTE: Possible underlying causes are numerous. Productive coughing should not be suppressed except in cases where the person's well-being may be compromised, such as with an aneurism or exhaustion.

- -

306. Dry cough – no phlegm production

If cough is due to throat irritation:

a. Blue ‖39‖ on #1-2-3.

If cough is due to heart/lung imbalance:

b. Green ‖32‖ systemic front.

c. Purple ‖63‖ on #4-5 (see attribute ‖63‖.

- -

307. Diverticulosis

a. Lemon ‖22‖ systemic front.

b. Yellow ‖18‖ and Indigo ‖44-47‖ on #9-10-18-19.

NOTE: In most cases an increase in dietary fiber is essential.

- -

308. Endometriosis

a. Lemon ‖22‖ and Magenta ‖64-68‖ systemic front.

b. Purple ‖54-62‖ on painful areas of misplaced endometrial tissue.

c. Indigo ‖44-47‖ on painful areas also may be tried. Surgical intervention may be required.

- -

309. Sickle cell anemia

a. Red ‖3‖ and Lemon ‖22‖ systemic front from #22.

b. Magenta ‖65-67‖ on #4-5-18.

c. Violet ‖48‖ on #6.

NOTE: This condition is considered incurable and life-shortening, but this schedule may be tried – with other Colors as symptoms dictate.

- -

310. Primary lymphedema

a. Yellow ‖17‖ and Lemon ‖22‖ systemic front to include affected extremity.

b. Magenta ‖65-67‖ on #4-5-18.

NOTE: Appropriate exercise may be helpful and even essential.

Color attribute number: ‖00‖. Tonation areas: #0-00.

311. Secondary lymphedema
   a. Yellow ||17|| and Lemon ||22|| systemic front to
       include affected extremity.
   b. Magenta ||65-67|| on #4-5-18, or Purple ||60|| if with high fever.
   c. If with fever, Blue ||39|| systemic front to include affected extremity.
   NOTE: Other diseases may be involved; surgery or radiation also can be
   causal.

- -

312. Cigarette smoking, tobacco
   a. Green ||29-31|| systemic front.
   b. Orange ||6|| and Lemon ||22-23|| on #4-5-17.
   NOTE: An authoritative medical opinion (Merck Manual) on the dismal
   health prospects of those who smoke more than one pack of cigarettes a day
   contends:

   1. Smokers have twenty times the likelihood of developing lung
   cancer, chronic bronchitis, and/or emphysema, compared to non-
   smokers. Less than a pack per day decreases the risk more-or-less, but
   every cigarette smoked adds its share of poisons to the body.
   2. Increases the risk of atherosclerosis and other vascular diseases, and
   may double the chance of having a heart attack (myocardial infarction).
   3. Pregnant women who smoke give birth to smaller infants, and
   increases the probability of miscarriage or stillbirth.
   4. Other disorders which occur more frequently in smokers include
   tuberculosis, cancer of the mouth or throat or bladder, stomach ulcers,
   optic nerve damage, gum problems leading to loss of teeth, and on and
   on and on.

It is difficult to imagine a substance with more insidious capability of harm
to good health than tobacco. While it may take years or decades for the
injury to become evident, the price for this folly eventually must be paid:
"As you sow, so shall you reap." The human body has an incredible
capacity for accepting abuse and repairing the damage, but when it has been
pushed past its limit we cannot intelligently expect to completely regain that
which has been wasted. Spectro-Chrome can help in most cases but its
value will be greatly diminished unless the use of tobacco in any form is
stopped. If the cause is not removed, the effects will persist. Tonate symptoms as they occur.

- -

**313. Nearsightedness (myopia), farsightedness (hyperopia), other visual
   refractive disorders (ametropia)**
   a. Lemon ||22|| systemic front, and
   b. Yellow ||16-17|| on #1 for two weeks, then
   c. Lemon ||22|| systemic front, and
   d. Orange ||15|| on #1 for four weeks, then
   e. Lemon ||22|| systemic front, and
   f. Red ||1|| on #1 for six weeks.
   g. Repeat above schedule as needed.   (Continued on next page)

h. In some cases a relaxant such as Violet ‖51‖ or Purple ‖54‖ on #1 may be useful.

NOTE: The extent of visual problems is often influenced by the person's general health so Lemon ‖22‖ systemic tonations are specified and may be essential. Improvement is likely but complete resolution is not.

- -

314. Discharges

Some conditions (splinters, wounds, leukorrhea, etc.) cause a discharge of pus or other matter. The following comprehensive schedule may be used in such cases.

With little or no fever:

a. Lemon ‖22‖ systemic to include affected area.

b. Blue ‖39‖ on affected area.

c. A few tonations of Orange ‖15‖ and/or Yellow ‖17‖ on affected area (or systemic) also may be used for a chronic condition.

When there is fever:

d. Green ‖32‖ and Blue ‖39‖ systemic to include affected area.

e. Magenta ‖65‖ on #4-5-18, or Purple ‖60‖ on #4-5 if fever is high.

When discharge shows signs of stopping:

f. Green ‖32‖ systemic to include affected area.

g. Indigo ‖44‖ on affected area.

NOTE: If condition recurs, repeat schedule with emphasis on instructions a. and c.

- -

315. Unexplained fever (FUO)

a. Green ‖29-32‖ and Blue ‖39‖ systemic front.

b. Magenta ‖65-67‖ on #4-5-18, or Purple ‖60‖ on #4-5 if fever is high.

c. If fever persists without explanation, try Yellow ‖17‖ systemic front. If fever does not drop, continue with instructions a. and b. for a few days, then repeat c.

d. If fever is a recurrent type, between episodes tonate Yellow ‖17‖, and Lemon ‖22‖ and Purple ‖61‖ systemic front.

- -

316. Pernicious anemia

a. Lemon ‖22‖ systemic front.

b. Orange ‖11‖ on #7-8.

c. Yellow ‖18‖ on #6-7-8-9-10.

NOTE: Possible causes include inadequate dietary vitamin B_{12}, inadequate stomach secretion of "intrinsic factor", intestinal worms, and myxedema.

- -

317. Earache

Any number of conditions may result in an earache. While the cause is being determined, tonate: (Continued on next page)

Color attribute number: ‖00‖. Tonation areas: #0-00.

a. Turquoise ‖33‖ systemic front.
b. Either: Orange ‖15‖ or Violet ‖51-52‖ on affected area.

- -

318. Syringomyelia
a. Sensory nervous system schedule (#275) systemic back.
b. Indigo ‖44‖ on affected area (syrinx).

- -

319. Urinary incontinence
     1) If due to sphincter weakness
a. Lemon ‖22‖ systemic front.
b. Orange ‖15‖ and Green ‖31‖ on #11.
c. Kegel's exercise may help in many cases.
     2) If due to nerve injury
d. Motor nervous system schedule (#276) systemic to
     include affected nerve areas.
     3) In men, if due to benign prostate enlargement, see schedule #142.
     4) In all cases, follow the recommendations in Chapter five, part one.
     Drinking tea is involved in some cases.

- -

320. Preventive tonations (prophylaxis)
     When completely healthy there may seem to be little point in taking
tonations. However, since many conditions take considerable time before becoming apparent, occasional (perhaps once a week) "preventive"
tonations may be a sensible practice.
a. Green ‖29‖ and Magenta ‖64‖ systemic front.
NOTE: Probably as important as tonations: 1) Put Chapter five (part one)
of this book into practice in your daily life; 2) develop a cheerful, positive
attitude in your thinking patterns; and 3) include vigorous exercise in your
day-to-day routine.

- -

321. Localized scratch dermatitis (localized neurodermatitis)
a. Green ‖29‖ and Magenta ‖64‖ systemic to include affected area.
b. Blue ‖37‖ on affected area.
NOTE: Emotional factors are usually involved; emotional stress must be
controlled. Patients at times may be unaware of their scratching (unconscious habit) so a bandage on the affected area may be helpful.

- -

322. Genital herpes. Herpes simplex
a. Green ‖32‖ and Blue ‖39‖ systemic until acute symptoms or apparent
effects of the disease disappear, then
b. Between relapses, which are common, tonate Yellow ‖17‖ and Lemon
‖22‖ systemic front for several months.
c. Indigo ‖45-47‖ on the affected area may be tried *at the first sign* of a
relapse.
NOTE: Tonate unusual symptoms by using Table of Attributes.

323. Phobias. Schizophrenia. Mental/emotional disorders

Spectro-Chrome most likely will need help for these conditions. Emotional disorders often have roots which may be difficult to identify. Behavioral modification methods frequently are effective. Depending on individual circumstances, one or more of these Colors may be tried (local or systemic): Yellow ‖20‖, Lemon ‖22‖, Purple ‖62‖, Magenta ‖64‖, Scarlet ‖77‖.

The Table of Color Attributes indicates the reason for considering each Color. DuoChrome (Chapter 13) with Green/Magenta is as yet untested but holds promise for these conditions.

— —

324. Candida (candidiasis)

The most common Candida is Albicans, and it can be involved in several serious disorders such as endocarditis, splenomegaly, anemia, fulminating septicemia, meningitis, nephritis, etc. Tonations must be tailored to the conditions; use the index of Color schedules, and the Table of Color Attributes for secondary conditions or symptoms.

— —

325. Digestive hyperacidity

If condition is acute:

a. Turquoise ‖33‖ systemic front.
b. Blue ‖39‖ and/or Indigo ‖44-47‖ on #6-7-8.

If condition is chronic:

c. Lemon ‖22‖ systemic front.
d. Blue ‖39‖ and/or Indigo ‖44-47‖ on #6-7-8.

NOTE: Dietary and emotional factors may be involved.

— —

326. Carpal tunnel syndrome. Dry-eye syndrome

a. Lemon ‖22‖ systemic front to include affected area.
b. Orange ‖15‖ on affected area.
c. Blue ‖39‖ on affected area if there is pain.

— —

327. Retinopathy

This condition can be the result of several other disorders such as diabetes, high blood pressure, arteriosclerosis. The underlying cause must be determined and tonated if possible. For the retinopathy:

a. Lemon ‖22‖ systemic front.
b. Sensory nervous system schedule #275 on #1.
c. Magenta ‖66‖ on #1-2-3-4-5.
d. Purple ‖55‖ on #1.
e. Indigo ‖44‖ on #1 if retinal hemorrhages occur.

10. A careful reading of this Chapter may well give the impression that there could be a schedule of Spectro-Chrome Colors for almost every imaginable ailment. Such an assumption would be correct because no matter what the problem is, there is a Spectro-Chrome Color (or Colors) which should be effective *if* the person has the necessary vitality *and* total or irreversible damage is not

present. The difficulty lies in determining whether the damage is in fact total or irreversible. The human body is designed in a truly magnificent manner, and when an appropriate agent is used, some disorders which are designated as incurable by other healing systems may be at least ameliorated. Spectro-Chrome can be expected to do *something* in almost every case.

11. In cases of paralysis caused by nerve dysfunction, favorable results only can be attained by their repair or by utilization of other nerves to the affected area. Even if responsive, these are characteristically slow processes requiring patience and perseverance.

12. There are disorders which may take years, even decades, to manifest themselves. Dinshah had a rule-of-thumb: each year of developmental time for a condition may take one month of tonations. The level of recovery depends, as mentioned, on the person's vitality, to what extent the disorder has progressed, and whether irreversible changes have occurred.

13. Some conditions such as hemophilia, Tay-Sachs' and other heredity-associated disorders, may not respond to Spectro-Chrome if there is a total lack of certain constitutional abilities. Color schedules for them are listed in the hope that a spark may exist which could be fanned into life by Spectro-Chrome. However, even when a disorder's cause cannot be corrected it does not imply that its consequences or symptoms can not be alleviated. There may be a Color schedule for a symptom, or the Color attributes (Chapter six) can be consulted for appropriate tonations for the affected organ or system.

14. The intent of these five paragraphs is to encourage a cautiously optimistic view, even when others label a condition as a "hopeless" or "incurable" case. Where there is life (and Spectro-Chrome) there is hope, or as Dr. Baldwin is quoted our preface, "...I do not feel justified in refusing any case without a trial."

✳   ✳   ✳   ✳   ✳

CHAPTER EIGHT

EQUIVALENT SOUNDS FOR COLORS

1. This Chapter describes another method of imparting energy (Sound) as a healing modality. There are also Color therapies which use other avenues; one of them shines Colors solely into the eyes, another uses Colors on nerve paths. The best known is "blue-light therapy" for neo-natal cases of jaundice, where Light acts directly on excess bilirubin by penetrating the skin. To some extent, these processes are also utilized in Spectro-Chrome therapy (if the eyes are open, in the first instance), but the major mechanism by which its effects are accomplished is described here, as well as the reasoning behind Sound as an complementary energy.

2. In music, an octave (diatonic scale) is the eighth note higher or lower than the first note sounded, and will have a frequency of double or half respectively of the first note. Generally, the word "octave" is used with reference to music, but in this Chapter we will take the liberty of using it to mean the doubling or halving of Light frequencies.

3. If you slowly depress a piano key (so it is not audible) and hold it down, then strike and release a key an octave higher or lower, an echo will be heard on the depressed key note. This phenomenon is known as "resonance". A well-tuned piano will resonate strongly while one badly out-of-tune may not at all.

4. Each cell in a living entity produces a specific radiant energy (its aura) when it is functioning correctly, but when there is a dysfunction its auric frequency or strength will change. The aggregate of a person's cellular radiant energy is their aura or (invisible) Color-balance frequency. When in good health and the forces of metabolism (anabolism and catabolism, construction and destruction, Red and Violet) are in balance, auric Color is balanced between Red and Violet: Magenta. During an illness of any kind it shifts toward either end of the spectrum, or its strength is altered.

5. The effects generated by Spectro-Chrome are induced by tonating Colors which are in resonance with the areas of the body which are underactive and in need of reinforcement, or by using opposite (interference) Colors on areas which are overactive. Spectro-Chrome Colors are not the same as the Colors of the aura but the resonance between them is in the same manner as the resonance echo between the piano notes. In one sentence, it is as simple as this: Spectro-Chrome Color frequencies resonate with auric Color frequencies.

6. By extension of this reasoning, Sound frequencies also should be a means of therapy. (Music therapy employing chords and their progressions is an entirely separate system.) It is not difficult to calculate the equivalent basic Sound frequency for each Color. The basic frequency of Spectro-Chrome Red is 436,803,079,680,000 cycles per second; to arrive at a frequency in the audible range, divide the basic figure by two 40 times (or by 1024 four times, or other equivalent equation). This gives the 40th octave lower of Red: 397.27 which falls in mid-range of many musical instruments. Other Spectro-Chrome Color/Sound equivalents were calculated similarly from the basic frequencies given in the **Spectro-Chrome Metry Encyclopedia** and are listed in the following table.

7. The four columns in the following table are: 1) Spectro-Chrome Color, 2) the Sound equivalent frequency, 3) the closest music note name, 4) the music note frequency. Use the frequencies in column two if a tone generator is available. A musical instrument able to produce a continuous tone, such as an organ, can be employed; the notes in column three are then used. They are not, however, likely to be quite the same as Spectro-Chrome Colors because of over-tones, under-tones, harmonics, and the lack of either-side frequencies. The notes in column three and frequencies in column four assume an instrument tuned to the widely used A-note pitch of 440 cycles per second. The figures are by calculation and not necessarily of a particular instrument, but are close enough for most purposes.

8. Human vision recognition frequencies do not span a full octave so neither do the notes required to generate Spectro-Chrome Color/Sound equivalents.

TABLE OF EQUIVALENT SOUNDS FOR COLORS

1) Spectro-Chrome Color:	2) Equivalent frequency:	3) Music note name:	4) Music note frequency:
Red	397.3	G	392
Orange	430.8	A	440
Yellow	464.4	A#	466
Lemon	497.9	B	494
Green	531.5	C	523
Turquoise	565.0	C#	554
Blue	598.6	D	587
Indigo	632.1	D#	622
Violet	665.7	E	659
Purple	565.0*	A# and E	562*
Magenta	531.5*	G and E	525*
Scarlet	497.9*	G# and D	501*

*Reverse polarity

9. Purple, Magenta, and Scarlet have both sides of the spectrum in their design so each requires two notes for comparable Sound production. They have the same frequencies as Turquoise, Green, and Lemon respectively but as Dinshah termed it, with "reverse polarities", which endows them with their unique capabilities. Rather than G, G# is used for Red when making Scarlet as it results in a closer Sound frequency. In theory, these three Colors (or Sounds) can be produced by adjusting the intensities of the two prime Colors (or Sounds), Red and Violet (or G and E). More complex equipment is required to create these composite frequencies in this manner, either with Light or Sound.

10. Sounds should not be expected to be nearly so effective as Colors for four reasons: 1) Sound and Color frequencies (except Red, Violet, and Magenta) should have a certain percentage of Green in their composition for best physiologic effect; 2) Sounds produced by musical instruments will contain vitiating overtones, harmonics, etc.; 3) Light energy is at a considerably higher potential than sound; 4) Sounds do not have intended either-side frequencies. For these reasons it is recommended that when Sound is used it be in conjunction with the equivalent Spectro-Chrome Color.

CHAPTER NINE

COLORS for ELEMENTS

1. When chemical elements are in a luminous, active state (ionized), each element emits a characteristic set of spectral Color lines which can be observed by use of an optical device: a spectroscope (there are also invisible lines). These are known as "Fraunhofer emission lines" and are always in the same relative positions in the spectrum of each element, somewhat like an identifying fingerprint. A compound will exhibit the lines of all its component elements.

2. Fraunhofer Lines normally are seen in a spectroscope as bright, colored bands of differing intensities. However, there is a technical procedure for shining white Light through the element under ionization which causes the bright lines to disappear and in their place are dark lines. Where the element had been emitting energy of certain frequencies (Fraunhofer emission lines), now it is absorbing the same frequencies from the Light energy; appropriately, the dark lines are called "Fraunhofer absorption lines".

3. Dinshah learned the scientific value of a spectroscope at an early age, and when Spectro-Chrome was being developed in the early 1900s this skill was employed with the innovative objective of equating elements with Colors. His reasoning: Since energy from Light can be absorbed by elements when they are in an active (ionized) state, it should follow that the live human body, with its electro-chemical generated emanations (aura), could be influenced by the application of Colors similar to the Fraunhofer lines of each element. He examined the Fraunhofer emission spectrum of each then known element, and with his thorough knowledge of chemistry, anatomy, physiology and medicine, assigned each element to the Color which most closely represented its effect on the body. The predominant position of Fraunhofer lines in each element's spectrum was used as the guide to their Spectro-Chrome Color placement. Some newly discovered elements were added in later years.

4. Here are some examples illustrating how his logic was implemented: Chapter six (Spectro-Chrome Color Attributes) lists "bone builder" under Orange and Lemon which the following table shows are the Colors for calcium and phosphorus respectively; these are essential elements of bones. Bromides are widely used as analgesics; Purple (soporific) is the Color predominance of bromine. Chlorine is used as a disinfectant, and is found as such in the Green section. Carbohydrates and hydrocarbons are basically hydrogen (Red) and carbon (Yellow) and are used by the body for fuel, so when there is a fever (a higher than normal level of fuel consumption) oxygen (Blue, opposite Color of Red) consumes the excess energy, producing water and carbon dioxide, and thereby eventually lowers the fever. This is of course a simplification as physiologic processes generally do not use elements as such, but Spectro-Chrome Colors/Elements as they are listed in the following table often can produce effects as though they did.

TABLE OF ELEMENTS BY SINGLE COLOR PREDOMINANCE

RED
Cadmium   Hydrogen   Krypton   Neon

ORANGE

Aluminum	Antimony	Arsenic	Boron	Calcium
Copper	Helium	Selenium	Silicon	Xenon

YELLOW

Beryllium	Carbon	Iridium	Magnesium	Molybdenum
Osmium	Palladium	Platinum	Rhenium	Rhodium
	Ruthenium	Sodium	Tin Tungsten	

LEMON

Cerium	Germanium	Gold	Hafnium	Iodine
Iron	Lanthanum	Neodymium	Phosphorus	Praseodymium
Protoactinium	Samarium	Scandium	Silver	Sulphur
Thorium	Titanium	Uranium	Vanadium	Yttrium
		Zirconium		

GREEN
Barium   Chlorine   Nitrogen   Radium   Tellurium   Thallium

TURQUOISE
Chromium   Fluorine   Mercury   Nickel   Niobium
Tantalum   Zinc

BLUE
Cesium   Indium   Oxygen

INDIGO
Bismuth   Ionium   Lead   Polonium

VIOLET
Actinium   Cobalt   Gallium   Radon

PURPLE
Bromine   Europium   Gadolinium   Terbium

MAGENTA
Lithium   Potassium   Rubidium   Strontium

SCARLET
Argon   Dysprosium   Erbium   Holmium   Lutecium
Manganese   Thulium   Ytterbium

CHAPTER TEN

THE LEFT WRISTWATCH

1. Acupuncture, acupressure, reflexology, iridology, and kinesiology have a similarity in that they all demonstrate how a cause in one part of the body can generate an effect in a distant part.

2. A graphic introduction to kinesiology may be performed by carefully following these directions:

A. Wear a wristwatch on your left wrist.

B. Stand up and extend your right arm straight out in front of yourself.

C. While you resist, have someone exert increasing pressure on your right hand until your right arm moves downward; take notice of how strong you are in opposing the pressure on your hand.

D. Remove the watch from your left wrist and now wear it on your right wrist (or do not wear it at all).

E. Repeat steps B/C/D and compare the effort it now takes you to resist the downward pressure with what it took when you had the watch on your left wrist.

3. I will not prejudice you by telling what the difference is likely to be. This demonstration has been successful with every person on whom I have tried it, but I understand that a few people have a reversed energy flow so the test will show reversed effects when the watch is on the right wrist compared to the left wrist. Left or right wrist, there will be a difference from one to the other.

4. Some believe that a mechanical watch rather than an electronic one must be used to achieve the effect, but I have noted the same consequence regardless of the type of watch (or even a bracelet). Try this with both types of watches and draw your own conclusion. Regardless of how it works for you, it is safer not to habitually wear metallic bands of any type on either wrist.

5. Procedures similar to this are used by some kinesiologists as a diagnostic method but that is beyond the scope of this book.

* * * * *

CHAPTER ELEVEN

A TRIUMPH for SPECTRO-CHROME

1. In the 12 years following the introduction of Spectro-Chrome in 1920, Dinshah taught 54 classes with a total of 1239 students in attendance (many more classes were held in succeeding years but most records were lost in the 1945 Institute fire). Among the students were numerous physicians, surgeons, dentists, and others allied to the health field. Two of his more notable graduates were Dr. Kate W. Baldwin in 1921, and her brother in 1922, Dr. L. Grant Baldwin, an eminent surgical/gynecological authority and a charter member of the American College of Surgeons–Mayo Clinics. He placed a number of Spectro-Chrome equipments in service in his Brooklyn NY clinic. She was for 23 years the senior surgeon at Philadelphia Woman's Hospital, and introduced Spectro-Chrome in that institution; she eventually had as many equipments in use there as space allowed, eleven more in her private practice as well as a few "loaners" for her patients unable to come to make office visits.

2. The following excerpts are from a Minutes volume of the Hospital's Board of Managers, photographically reproduced and somewhat reduced in size to fit these pages. (Dinshah subpoenaed the Minutes to aid his defense in the 1947 Camden NJ trial; the Hospital did not request its return so he kept the book and we have it now.) The Managers' meetings with discussions relating to Spectro-Chrome were held over a period of about three years (page numbers and dates have been added):

Page 43; November 23, 1923

Miss Saunders spoke of Dr. Baldwin's desire to come before the Board and explain the use of the Spectraphone method. Mrs. Shoemaker moved that Dr. Baldwin be granted this privilege at the next meeting.

Page 49; December 21, 1923

The regular meeting of the Board of Managers of the Woman's Hospital of Phila. was held on Friday, December 21, 1923 with Miss Saunders in the Chair and nineteen managers present. Before the regular business, Dr. Baldwin gave an illustrated account of the wonderful work done in the Hospital with the spectrochrome. She described a remarkable case of a child (Grace) who was so badly burned that there seemed no hope of her recovery. With the use of the Spectrochrome the child is almost entirely cured. It is such an unusual case that the Board feels it should be written up for publication by Dr. Baldwin. The child was brought into the meeting and undressed so that the Managers could see the enormous area which had been healed. The Spectrochrome is used in no other Hospital and great credit should be given Dr. Baldwin for developing its use here. There are four instruments in the Hospital and more could be used if the room were larger.

Page 65; March 28, 1924

be made. Seconded by Mrs. Slade and passed. There was also a letter

from the Staff asking that

1. Ward patients pay $3. a day and semi-private patients
   $4 to $5 a day.
2. Ward patients pay in advance and private patients also
   when advisable.
3. The radium be used outside the hospital for one year
   paying $3\frac{1}{4}\%$ insurance instead of 2%.
4. The Board purchase a radium needle and that the balance of the radium fund be invested in Liberty Bonds.
5. The Board request Dr. Baldwin to discontinue the use
   of the spectrochrome therapy on account of the article
   in the medical journal.

Mrs. Shoemaker moved that the rates be raised. Seconded

and passed. Mrs. Slade moved that the patients pay in advance.

Seconded by Miss Biddle and passed. It was decided to let the radium

go outside the hospital at the increased premium. It was agreed

to purchase the radium needle. The matter of asking Dr. Baldwin

to discontinue the use of spectrochrome therapy was left to a com-

mittee composed of Mrs. Shoemaker, chairman, Mrs. Stone and Mrs.

Tatum.

Page 69; April 28, 1924

Mrs. Shoemaker reported progress on the spectrochrome

therapy and this matter was left in the hands of the committee for

a further report in May.

Page 73; May 23, 1924

Mrs. Shoemaker, for the Committee to investigate the

Spectrochrome Therapy, said that the question had been considered

from every viewpoint and that the Committee recommended the con-

tinuance of present conditions. This report of the Committee was

accepted.

Page 101; March 27, 1925

Dr. Baldwin in a letter spoke of her need of more room for the Spectro-chrome. She asked to have two cubicles made; she is getting many cases and needs more room. Mrs. Shoemaker moved that this matter be left with the clinics committee. Motion carried. Miss Plumer moved that the Clinics Committee also have the power to act. Motion carried.

Page 162; September 24, 1926

Letter from the Internes, objecting to Dr. Baldwin's presence on the Surgical Staff. Mrs. Earle moved that the Board of Managers request Dr. Bald-win's resignation from the Surgical Staff, if such request meets the approval of the majority of the General Staff and that Dr. Baldwin be granted the privi-lege of practising Spectro-chrome Therapy with her private patients in the Woman's Hospital. This motion was seconded and carried.

Adjournment.

Page 165; October 22, 1926

At a special meeting of the Board, Mrs. Kirk moved that Dr. Baldwin's resignation be accepted with regret. The motion was seconded and carried.

Elizabeth Booth La
Recording Secretary.

Page 177; January 27, 1927

A letter from the Spectro-chrome Therapists was read, deploring the action of the Woman's Hospital in requesting the resignation of Dr. Baldwin. It was suggested that Miss Bodine be instructed to write to the above association, en-closing Dr. Baldwin's appreciative letter to us and also stating that we had offered Dr. Baldwin a special department for her spectrochrome work.

KATE W. BALDWIN, M.D., F.A.C.S

Fellow, American Medical Association; Fellow, Academy of
Ophthalmology and Otolaryngology, etc.
Senior Surgeon, Woman's Hospital, Philadelphia Pennsylvania

3. As may be seen from the foregoing paragraphs, Spectro-Chrome received enthusiastic support for years at Philadelphia Woman's Hospital (later merged with another hospital). The decline began in 1924 when, without investigation into its possible merits, an extremely derogatory article to Dinshah and Spectro-Chrome appeared in the American Medical Association Journal (mentioned in the Minutes of March 28, 1924). Eventually, given the choice, Dr. Baldwin resigned her prestigious hospital position rather than accede to the interns' demand that she give up her beloved Spectro-Chrome in favor of her surgical duties. That the Board of Managers was indisputably convinced regarding the therapeutic value of Spectro-Chrome is amply documented in the Minutes, and emphasized by their offer to allow Dr. Baldwin to continue with Spectro-Chrome for her private patients at the hospital after she resigned from the staff (Minutes page 162, 9/24/26). That could have been the end of this narrative, but it is not.

4. Dr. Baldwin continued with her medical/Spectro-Chrome practice; and Dinshah continued to promote Spectro-Chrome: lecturing, teaching classes, designing new projectors and accessories, and the day-to-day supervision of his Institute. The problem now was the increasing pressure from opposing elements. In May of 1930 Dinshah was arrested and jailed in Buffalo, New York. The indictment charged he "...did feloniously steal $175.00 from Housman Hughes by falsely representing and pretending that a certain instrument and machine [Spectro-Chrome] would cure any and all human disease and ailments...", with further charges regarding the filters.

5. One of his graduates, Dr. Welcome A. Hanor, posted bail ($1500) for Dinshah who was then released from jail. Completely undaunted, Dinshah resumed his usual duties while awaiting the setting of a trial date, including conducting ten more classes.

6. The trial began on Tuesday, April 28, 1931. If he lost the case, Dinshah faced the possibility of 10 years' imprisonment and a $10,000 fine. Nonetheless, he proceeded to defend himself by acting as his own attorney. In later years, when asked why he conducted his own defense, he often said, "The judge knows the *law*, and *I know my science* so I can defend it better than any lawyer; Truth may be defeated but never conquered", or words to that effect.

7. The prosecution produced five witnesses in an effort to prove Spectro-Chrome was valueless and that the filters did not produce monochromes (as they mistakenly expected). A physicist testified that the bulb in the Spectro-Chrome equipment was an ordinary incandescent lamp (the defense never claimed otherwise), and that the filters were of ordinary glass and not capable of producing spectral (Fraunhofer) emission lines (which also was never claimed). Another witness was a physician who treated patients with ultra-violet rays, radium, and x-rays. He thought Colors as therapeutic agents would have no curative effects but admitted not having used Spectro-Chrome to arrive at this "expert" opinion. Three witnesses, including the complainant – Housman Hughes, who never even took or gave a single tonation – recounted statements made by Dinshah regarding the effects of Spectro-Chrome, how the effects are generated, the procedure for leasing Spectro-Chrome equipments, and other non-technical details. That was the case against Dinshah and Spectro-Chrome. Together, the five testimonies were supposed to be strong enough to convict him and condemn his System (a sixth witness was called later for rebuttal). It appeared to be an open-and-shut

case: How could a sensible jury believe that an ordinary Light-bulb and five pieces of colored glass be of any use in healing the sick?! Now it was time for Dinshah to prove not only that they could but in fact they did. The prosecution was about to receive a surprise.

8. Dinshah began his defense with a licensed physician and Spectro-Chrome Institute graduate, Dr. Welcome A. Hanor. His testimony recounted excellent results in nine years' experience with Spectro-Chrome (burns, arthritis, diabetes, cancer, tuberculosis, dementia, heart disorders, stomach ulcers, etc.), some cases pronounced by other practitioners as "hopeless", and a few which were beyond help of any system. His most telling remark was, "I should hate to practice without it [Spectro-Chrome]". He also outlined some of Dinshah's theories and classroom teachings.

9. In 1944, Dinshah published the transcript of proceedings of this lawsuit, with his comments, and titled it **Triumph of Spectro-Chrome**. It is out-of-print due to the 1945 Institute fire (it will be reprinted), but the testimony of Dinshah's next witness was of such strength that it merits your attention. From a surviving copy, the text has been reproduced here (nouns are capitalized in keeping with Dinshah's style; Chapter numbers are from the original volume):

CHAPTER 13

HOSPITAL SENIOR SURGEON CHAMPIONS SPECTRO-CHROME

The second Witness for the Defendant must have been an unexpected surprise to the Honorable Prosecuting Attorney, as well as the Honorable Court. It was a turn of such weight and power, that even the hearers in the Court Room could not but express their feelings on their faces. A modest, unassuming woman took the stand. Her name was announced as Doctor Kate W. Baldwin and having been sworn for the Defendant, the Testimony commenced.

DINSHAH – Where do you live?

BALDWIN – Philadelphia, Pennsylvania.

DINSHAH – Madam, what year did you graduate in Philadelphia, Pennsylvania?

BALDWIN – Medical College?

DINSHAH – In what year?

BALDWIN – 1890.

DINSHAH – You have been 40 years as an active Physician?

BALDWIN – Yes, sir

DINSHAH – And your special line is Surgery?

BALDWIN – Well, I am rated by the American College of Surgeons as a Surgeon, as a Fellow by the American Academy of Ophthalmology and Oto-Laryngology; I have never confined myself, however, exactly to Surgery.

JUSTICE – Forty-one years of general medical practice, is that right?

BALDWIN – Yes and Surgery.

DINSHAH – You were the Senior Surgeon of the Woman's Hospital of Philadelphia?

BALDWIN – Yes, sir.

DINSHAH – How many years, did you remain in charge of the Surgical Ward of the Woman's Hospital of Philadelphia?

BALDWIN – I was the Senior Surgeon for 23 years. I had a Clinic for almost the whole – for over 30 years, almost from the time I graduated, I was in clinical work.

DINSHAH – During the time that you were in charge of the Surgical work, you performed numerous Operations in Surgery – Major Surgery?

BALDWIN – Pretty nearly everything from the Crown of the Head, to the Soles of the Feet.

DINSHAH – You are also a Fellow of the American Medical Association?

BALDWIN – Yes, sir.

DINSHAH – And a Life Member of the Maryland Academy of Sciences?

BALDWIN – Yes, sir.

DINSHAH – What other medical and scientific qualifications have you, madam?

BALDWIN – I don't know just what you mean.

DINSHAH – What other affiliations in Medicine and Surgery have you?

BALDWIN – Well, I belong to the County and State Medical Societies of Pennsylvania; I am also registered in Pennsylvania, New York and Rhode Island, to practice Medicine and Surgery. I had my Interns' service at the Polytechnic Hospital, which is a Post-Graduate Hospital. I also had clinical work in Boston, in the city Hospital there and I belong to the American Academy of Ophthalmology and Oto-Laryngology. I was the first woman to be admitted to that organization. I am a Member of the American College of Surgeons and of the American Medical Association and various smaller societies, which perhaps you do not need to mention.

DINSHAH—Thank you. Now, in your surgical work, in the Woman's Hospital of Philadelphia—do I understand that the Woman's Hospital of Philadelphia is the oldest in the Country?

BALDWIN—It is the oldest, women's Hospital.

DINSHAH—It is the oldest, women's Hospital. What year was it established?

BALDWIN—I can not tell you.

DINSHAH—1850?

BALDWIN—About that time.

DINSHAH—And you were in charge of the surgical work of that Hospital for 23 years?

BALDWIN—Of the general Surgery.

DINSHAH—Of the general Surgery?

BALDWIN—Of the general surgical work; that did not include the Gynecological Surgery as far as the—

DINSHAH—General Major Surgery, really?

BALDWIN—General Major Surgery.

DINSHAH—Madam, how did you happen to meet me, the Defendant at the Bar?

BALDWIN—Some acquaintances of mine I met one evening and they said, "Doctor Baldwin, I think that there are some Lectures going on in town that you might be interested in. There is a man here who lectured at a certain place last week and he is coming back again this week and his subject in general, I think, is one that would interest you." So, I went to hear you, your talk then. Your subject was almost entirely on Occult Subjects, I think and the Ethical Society perhaps brought you there. In the course of those Lectures, I questioned very much whether—I liked Colonel Dinshah well enough, but, there were some things I did not like; there are other things—

JUSTICE—When did you get in touch with him? What we are interested in here, I take it, is when did you get in touch with the use of this Machine of his?

DINSHAH—When did you get in touch with me about the Spectro-Chrome System?

BALDWIN—Why, that is just what I am getting at. Now, you were delivering this Course of Lectures, you had one of the Spectro-Chrome Machines of a different type than this in the room and you at the last Lecture said something regarding the use of it as a therapeutic measure and another Doctor and myself in the audience went up to you and asked you, why you would not—if you would give a Course on the Therapeutics of Color in Philadelphia. Your reply was, "Yes, if you can get up a Class, I shall be glad to do so." I said, "I will be one of it." The other Doctor said, he would be another one and from that you had your first Class in Philadelphia of some eighty, I think somewhere along there, people.

DINSHAH—And there were numerous Doctors in it?

BALDWIN—There was quite a number of Doctors in it.

DINSHAH—Dental Surgeons?

JUSTICE—What year was that?

BALDWIN—That was in 1820.

DINSHAH—1921?

BALDWIN—1921, yes. Not 1820. I got my centuries mixed!

DINSHAH—1921, before you discovered the Origination of Spectro-Chrome?

BALDWIN—Yes.

DINSHAH—There were Dental Surgeons in it?

BALDWIN—Yes, sir.

DINSHAH—Medical Doctors?

BALDWIN—Yes, sir.

DINSHAH—Surgeons?

BALDWIN—Yes, sir.

DINSHAH—And lay people?

BALDWIN—Yes, sir.

DINSHAH—After you took the work, you took to the practice of Spectro-Chrome Metry, in your own private practice, as well as your Hospital work?

BALDWIN—Yes, sir.

DINSHAH—That was not a Machine like that? Kindly look at it (indicating). It was not invented at that time, in 1921?

BALDWIN—That Machine did not exist at that time.

DINSHAH—When I told one of the Classes in which you were present, that is one of the Meetings, that I had now perfected a Motor-driven Machine that would give much better facility for work, who placed the first order for this Equipment with me, without seeing it?

BALDWIN – I have the first Machine of that kind that was made.

DINSHAH – You have the first Machine exactly of that type?

BALDWIN – Yes, sir.

DINSHAH – Was it delivered to you in 1922?

BALDWIN – I couldn't say as to that. About that time.

DINSHAH – About that. If I said you had that Machine in your hands since about eight years, seven or eight years, would that be right?

BALDWIN – Yes.

DINSHAH – Did you use that Equipment with Slide-Carrier just like this (indicating)? Kindly examine the Glasses and see if those are similar to what you have?

BALDWIN – I should say it was.

DINSHAH – Sealed like that also?

BALDWIN – Yes, sir.

DINSHAH – All Slide-Carriers are sealed that way?

BALDWIN – Yes, sir.

DINSHAH – How many such Equipments did you get from the Institute since then?

BALDWIN – Well, I am running eleven every day! And I have several others that I put in homes, where people can not come to me.

DINSHAH – About how many in all, Spectro-Chrome Equipments?

BALDWIN – Different kinds of Equipment, not of that kind.

DINSHAH – Have you three like that?

BALDWIN – Yes, sir; I have five of them.

DINSHAH – You have five like that?

BALDWIN – Yes, sir.

DINSHAH – Purchased, taken from the Institute at various times, for your work there?

BALDWIN – Yes, sir.

DINSHAH – And you have other Spectro-Chromes, with different arrangement of the work?

BALDWIN – Yes, Colors being the same.

DINSHAH – The Color Slides being the same?

JUSTICE – You use eleven every day?

BALDWIN – Yes, sir.

DINSHAH – Using eleven Instruments every day?

BALDWIN – Using eleven Instruments every day; not all of that type.

DINSHAH – But you have five like that in use?

BALDWIN – I have five like that in use.

DINSHAH – Did you use that in the Hospital where you were?

BALDWIN – Not this type.

DINSHAH – No, the other type that you had?

BALDWIN – I did, yes, sir.

DINSHAH – With the same kind of Slides?

BALDWIN – Yes, sir.

DINSHAH – Same Color Slides?

BALDWIN – Yes, sir.

DINSHAH – Do you remember a case of Burns of a girl, Grace Shirlow by name?

BALDWIN – Yes, sir.

DINSHAH – Produce the Pictures of the condition of the girl and what you did. (Baldwin produces the Pictures.)

DINSHAH – I present to you, please, Doctor – these will have to be separated – this picture. Do you identify the girl that is shown there, as the condition of the girl after she was burnt by fire (showing Photogram to Witness)?

BALDWIN – Yes, sir.

DINSHAH – How much was she burnt in the front, in that picture as you made?

BALDWIN – About four-fifths of the Torso was burnt; that is, the Trunk. This represents the middle of the Body here (indicating). She was burnt beyond the middle of the Body; it went up to the Clavicle and under the Arm.

JUSTICE – That is the Shoulder Blade, as we call it?

BALDWIN – No, the Clavicle. The Shoulder Blade is on the Back.

DINSHAH – Collar Bone?

BALDWIN – Collar Bone, and it went from the Elbow up clear into the Axillary, down to the Groin, about four inches on the Left Leg, back up onto the Back and around onto this side (indicating); to make it brief, as near as I can, there was about that much (indicating) of the Trunk of the Body, the Torso, as we call it and up to here (indicating) that was not burned; all through here and on the left side of the Back, it was not only the Skin that was destroyed, but, the Fascia of the Muscle –

DINSHAH – What do you mean by Fascia?

BALDWIN – The covering of the Muscle, so that the little Muscle Fibers were exposed.

DINSHAH – Just a minute, please. This is the front of that girl (showing Photogram to Witness)?

BALDWIN – That is the front.

DINSHAH – This is the back (showing another photogram to Witness)?

BALDWIN – Yes, sir.

DINSHAH – Identify those Photograms,

please.

(The referred PHOTOGRAMS were marked Defendant's Exhibits 26 and 27 for Identification.) [See Addendum for relevant photos.]

BALDWIN – May I make one Statement, in regard to that picture?

DINSHAH – Yes, please, while I am exhibiting.

BALDWIN – That picture was not taken until two weeks after the Burn.

DINSHAH – So really the Burn was more severe than that?

BALDWIN – The Burn was more severe than that. I had cleared up quite a little in the two weeks.

JUSTICE – Do you want to offer them in Evidence, Doctor?

DINSHAH – Yes, I did have them in Evidence.

JUSTICE – Go right along with your questions. They can examine it.

DINSHAH – This case was brought to you and it came under your surgical care?

BALDWIN – Yes, sir.

DINSHAH – By looking at that case, from your surgical experience and your knowledge of Surgery, did you believe that any method known to Medicine and Surgery, could have kept that child alive?

BALDWIN – It is generally conceded, that with that much of the Body burned, even though the surface only may be involved, can not be saved.

DINSHAH – That is, it was an absolutely hopeless, fatal case?

BALDWIN – In was an absolutely hopeless fatal case. In fact, I got that about 24 hours after the Burn and the Surgeon or the Doctor who had been called in, went out very legitimately, just simply wrapped it up in gauze and cotton to protect it, as he was quite justified in saying, "There is no use in trying to do anything with this!" In fact, the dressing was so tightly pressed into the raw surface, that it was two weeks before I succeeded in getting it all off, as I would not force it off. I had to wait until the healing process took place underneath and it loosened up, because if you pulled off the dressings, you would pull off new Tissues, as well as old.

JUSTICE – You did use this Machine or a similar Machine, in connection with the treatment of that case?

BALDWIN – I used it entirely. I said to myself, "There is nothing in regular Medicine or Surgery, that can make that child live. If I can make it live, it has got to be by something else". Spectro-Chrome Metry was the thing I was working with at the time and I said to my Assistant, "We will see what Spectro-Chrome will do". That child had absolutely nothing but Color and Diet and dressing of sterilized waxed paper all through. We put a sheet of paper and a sheet of cloth and put in a Sterilizer; it took out the Paraffin, whatever it was made of, out and left just a sterilized, absorbent paper, very thin. You could see the Tissues underneath to a certain extent. We had some Sterilized Cocoa Nut Oil, which we ran this paper through. It was so light in weight, but letting it go a little beyond the Burn, it did not break off, it would stick to the Burn. If in a new dressing, there was any place that stuck, that had not loosened up, we go around it and let it stay on. That child's Elimination was kept perfect. She had two and three good Bowel Eliminations, in the course of 24 hours. She was put on a special diet and she was given all the Lemonade, sweetened with Brown Sugar, that she could have. That was her principal drink. She had all of that she wanted. Do you wish me to go on with the treatment?

DINSHAH – What did you use exclusively for building the Skin?

BALDWIN – Well, we had to get rid of –

DINSHAH – I mean, what System did you use? Did you use any Medicine or Surgery, for building the Skin?

BALDWIN – I used no Surgery at all.

JUSTICE – That is, you just used this treatment you have described, Doctor?

BALDWIN – I used this treatment.

JUSTICE – Just oil paper to cover, to keep the air from it and application of Color Rays?

BALDWIN – That is all, yes. Just for a minute; we did put a garment over. We could not put a bandage on that, you know, because it would give her Pain, so we simply laid down one or two thicknesses of gauze on the bed and put her on it and another over and the Nurse sewed it up like sort of a little Kimono, that simply protected her a little bit from the air. No bandages were used, because they would have added Pain rather than otherwise.

DINSHAH – You know this, you were taught this Spectro-Chrome Therapeutical System Chart (indicating)?

BALDWIN – Yes.

DINSHAH – Did you use this to select your [Color] Waves?

BALDWIN–Yes.

DINSHAH–Will you kindly tell the Honorable Court and the Jury, what Wave you picked out to build the Skin?

BALDWIN–We used the Turquoise principally to build the Skin.

DINSHAH–That is what you were taught?

BALDWIN–Yes, that is what I was taught.

DINSHAH–How is a Turquoise produced by that Instrument–of what Colors combined?

BALDWIN–Green, and Blue added to Green.

DINSHAH–And that makes this Turquoise Color?

BALDWIN–That makes the Turquoise.

DINSHAH–And it is that that built the Skin, on this girl, exclusively?

BALDWIN–No; may have built the Skin exclusively. We had to use other Colors to stimulate the separation of the Sloughs off Body and get rid of that–that dead Tissue, before you can build new. New Epithelium, new Skin, will not cover over dead Tissue and we had to stimulate that separation by using Stimulating Colors.

JUSTICE–Turquoise was produced, you say, Green on Blue?

BALDWIN–Green and Blue, and her general System had to be kept up. We had to pay attention to her Heart condition, to keep that up. I used other things than just simply the Turquoise, but the Turquoise was the thing that probably built the Skin in the end. There has never been known a case, as far as Medicine and Surgery goes, that covered as much surface of the Body that was burned, that has ever gotten well. A good many Surgeons saw the case and the general opinion was that–well, I know one Surgeon, been in the War, he had been all over everywhere, says, "Well, we don't try to treat one of those; we give them just a big dose of Morphine and push them off to one side."

DINSHAH–You used Spectro-Chrome on this girl exclusively, without any medical or surgical treatment of any kind?

BALDWIN–No; I was criticized for not Skin Grafting, but what could I get Skin Graft there? No place to Skin Graft.

DINSHAH–You used only the Spectro-Chrome System?

BALDWIN–I used only the Spectro-Chrome System.

DINSHAH–As taught by Dinshah?

BALDWIN–As taught by Dinshah. The first day she was in the Hospital, I was out of town

and she was nervous and the Intern did not know what to do, had to resort to some Bromide.

DINSHAH–You did not give it?

BALDWIN–But she had it, whether I gave it or not. The first day, she was left in the Intern's care and the first day that she was in, I was out of town and the Intern gave her either three or five Grains of Bromide of Sodium. With that exception, that Child had not one single thing, except her diet and Spectro-Chrome with the oiled paper.

DINSHAH–Who taught that Diet System to you?

BALDWIN–You did.

DINSHAH–How long did it take to complete the building of the Body of this girl, Doctor, so that she could wear a garment again?

BALDWIN–About seven months.

DINSHAH–Seven months?

BALDWIN–It would not have taken that long, had the child–had we been able to give the child the care that a private patient with a private Nurse would have had. We were very scarce of Nurses, as all Hospitals were at that time. She had to take whatever she could get, of whatever Nurse had to be on duty.

DINSHAH–Just a minute, please, Doctor. We shall curtail the Examination. You see, I want to save the time. Now, do you remember an incident, during this rebuilding of this Skin process, where the Health Authorities did something to this girl and something happened?

BALDWIN–Yes. There was a case of Diphtheria in the Ward and without saying anything to me about it, they knew I did not approve of Injections by Interns, so they went around and gave every child in the place a dose of Antitoxin.

DINSHAH–Did Grace Shirlow get it too?

BALDWIN–Grace Shirlow did.

DINSHAH–Without your knowledge or consent?

BALDWIN–Yes, sir.

DINSHAH–And what happened to her?

BALDWIN–She had run up a High Temperature and was very, very much worse in every way.

BALDWIN–What was the Temperature in Degrees?

BALDWIN–105 and 106.

DINSHAH–What brought it down to normal?

BALDWIN–Spectro-Chrome.

DINSHAH–Did you use the Blue Color to reduce this Temperature?

BALDWIN–I probably ran it down lower than the Blue Color.

DINSHAH–Used Indigo Color also?

BALDWIN–Indigo; yes, sir.

DINSHAH–You used Blue also?

BALDWIN–I used Turquoise, Blue, Indigo and Violet.

DINSHAH–According to the requirement?

BALDWIN–According to the requirement.

DINSHAH–As taught by my system in the Class?

BALDWIN–Yes, sir.

DINSHAH–And that brought it down to normal?

BALDWIN–Yes, sir.

DINSHAH–Will you please identify these two pictures, of the Front and Back of the girl, as she was when restored by Spectro-Chrome (showing pictures to Witness)?

BALDWIN–Yes.

DINSHAH–I offer them as Exhibits.

(The PHOTOGRAMS referred were received in Evidence and marked Defendant's Exhibits 28 and 29.) [See photos in Addendum.]

BALDWIN–There is no Cheloid there, Judge, at all or any Adhesions to the Tissues below.

DINSHAH–Was the Skin just like an ordinary Skin, moveable?

BALDWIN–It was perfectly moveable.

DINSHAH–It was not merely a Scar Tissue, but a real Skin?

BALDWIN–Yes.

DINSHAH–Thank you. Now, since that period, when you started to experiment about and get the evidence in Spectro-Chrome, I am naming certain things here and you may simply answer by "yes" or "no" whether you used it for these Disorders, because we do not have to waste time by going into details of medical work. Did you have cases of Cataract of the Eyes, restored to normal by Spectro-Chrome?

BALDWIN–Yes.

DINSHAH–Glaucoma or Hardening of the Eyeballs?

BALDWIN–Yes.

DINSHAH–Acute Infections affecting the Eyes?

BALDWIN–Yes.

DINSHAH–Hemorrhages in the Eyes, that is Bleeding?

BALDWIN–Yes.

DINSHAH–About the Ears–any Mastoid Trouble, behind the Ears?

BALDWIN–Yes.

DINSHAH–Otitis Media, meaning Inflammation in the Middle Ear?

BALDWIN–Yes.

DINSHAH–Any Tonsils and Adenoids?

BALDWIN–Yes.

DINSHAH–Did you have any experience in the Hospitals or in cases in treating Bronchial or Lung Troubles?

BALDWIN–Yes, I had some advanced cases of Tuberculosis.

DINSHAH–Bronchitis, I mean, Bronchitis, Inflammation of the Bronchial Passages?

BALDWIN–Yes, sir.

DINSHAH–Did you get any cases of Pleurisy?

BALDWIN–Yes.

DINSHAH–Any advanced cases of Tuberculosis, where cavities were formed and proved to be existent by X-Rays, in the Lungs?

BALDWIN–Yes, sir.

DINSHAH–Did you use the Spectro-Chrome for Functional Disorders of the heart?

BALDWIN–Yes.

DINSHAH–Did you use the Spectro-Chrome for any Organic Disorders of the Heart?

BALDWIN–Yes.

DINSHAH–Now, did you have occasion to use Spectro-Chrome for Gastric Ulcers?

BALDWIN–Yes.

DINSHAH–That is, Ulcers in the Stomach?

BALDWIN–Yes.

DINSHAH–Cancerous conditions?

BALDWIN–Yes.

DINSHAH–Piles or Hemorrhoids in the Rectal Region?

BALDWIN–Yes.

DINSHAH–Abscesses and Carbuncles on the Back, that big or that big (illustrating with fist) about say, two to three inches in diameter?

BALDWIN–I had Carbuncles that reached from here to here (indicating) and from the Occiput down to the Cervical.

DINSHAH–Would that be about that big or about that big (illustrating with fist)?

BALDWIN–Hardly, spread your hand. Large Carbuncles on the Neck, that very large one here on the Neck (indicating); they have them other places.

DINSHAH–You used Spectro-Chrome for that also?

BALDWIN–Yes, sir.

DINSHAH–Suppression of Urine in this burned girl; was that relieved by Spectro-Chrome?

BALDWIN–Yes, sir.

DINSHAH – Did you use this for the correction of Opium, Morphine and other Drug Habits?

BALDWIN – Yes, sir.

DINSHAH – Did you use Spectro-Chrome for any cases of Paralysis or Palsy?

BALDWIN – Yes, sir.

DINSHAH – Did you get under your surgical treatment there with Spectro-Chrome, any cases of Asthma?

BALDWIN – Yes, sir.

DINSHAH – Hay Fever?

BALDWIN – Yes.

DINSHAH – Common Colds?

BALDWIN – Yes.

DINSHAH – Laryngitis?

BALDWIN – Yes.

DINSHAH – All sorts of Infections?

BALDWIN – Yes.

DINSHAH – Mouth Disorders?

BALDWIN – Yes.

DINSHAH – Rheumatism, Lumbago and such other Infective Disorders with Rheumatic Fevers?

BALDWIN – Yes.

DINSHAH – Did you have any girl's case of Gonorrhea?

BALDWIN – Yes.

DINSHAH – What was the age of the girl?

BALDWIN – Eight years old.

DINSHAH – Eight years old with Gonorrhea? What did you do for her?

BALDWIN – Spectro-Chrome.

DINSHAH – Did you have a woman's case there, at the time Grace Shirlow was there, who had Syphilis?

BALDWIN – Yes.

DINSHAH – When I came to the Hospital, to see Grace Shirlow, do you remember showing me the case of a woman, who was burned by Radium and X-Rays, so that her Palate was ulcerated and so on?

BALDWIN – That one with the roof of the mouth gone?

DINSHAH – Yes. Was not one burnt by Radium and X-Ray?

BALDWIN – The one with the Clavicle and whole front of the Body and down the Arm here, that was an X-Ray Burn.

DINSHAH – Did you use Spectro-Chrome for that dangerous case also?

BALDWIN – Yes, sir.

DINSHAH – What was the result?

BALDWIN – It finally healed.

DINSHAH – So, in fact, without going into medical details and so on, you have used Spectro-Chrome in very many of these cases and in fact dangerous cases?

BALDWIN – Yes.

DINSHAH – What has been your experience in the use of the System?

BALDWIN – Absolutely satisfactory. They will always need an undertaker. We do not claim that, you know.

DINSHAH – Beg your pardon?

BALDWIN – We will always need the undertaker. We do not claim that we will not, but anything that is in human possibility to be put in a normal shape, it can be done with Spectro-Chrome better than it can with anything else and with many, many cases, it is the only thing that would put the patient in a condition to function.

DINSHAH – You had experience in Venereal Disorders?

BALDWIN – Yes, sir.

DINSHAH – What was your experience with Spectro-Chrome, in tonating those cases?

BALDWIN – They came out all right.

DINSHAH – Then, in fact, you will correct me if I am wrong, that you are still using Spectro-Chrome, stronger than ever?

BALDWIN – I use practically nothing else.

DINSHAH – But Spectro-Chrome?

BALDWIN – But Spectro-Chrome.

DINSHAH – Now, I shall show to you this Chart again –

JUSTICE – That is Exhibit 10.

DINSHAH – Your Honor, People's Exhibit 10; yes, sir.

JUSTICE – So as to identify the Chart.

DINSHAH – Yes, sir, People's Exhibit 10.

DINSHAH – This Spectro-Chrome Therapeutic System, in your experience and knowledge as a Physician, looking to the Physiological Effects produced by these Color Waves, did you find that these effects are actually produced or did you find that the Chart is humbug?

BALDWIN – In all general ways, the Chart is **not** a humbug – absolutely.

DINSHAH – What is your experience from the results?

BALDWIN – My experience from the results is, that the Chart is correct.

DINSHAH – You were in the Class in Philadelphia. Did your interest increase so much, that you wanted to repeat it, for your own knowledge?

BALDWIN – Yes, sir.

DINSHAH – How many Classes and Courses did you take and pay for in full?

BALDWIN – Five.

DINSHAH – You paid me for all of them?

BALDWIN – I paid you for five in full. I took one Course afterwards by your invitation.

DINSHAH – And what was the purpose in repeating the Courses?

BALDWIN – That I might get more general knowledge.

DINSHAH – Was it necessary that you should repeat them?

BALDWIN – I probably learned a good deal, but I may say, all my good work, was done before I repeated, but I do not think you can ever stop learning. If the Doctors stop learning, when they came out of Medical College, they would know mighty little; they would be of mighty little good to the community, less than they are as it is.

DINSHAH – Do you know as a Physician in your County and State work with other Medical Societies, whether your friend Doctors are also using now various systems of Color and Light, for healing purposes?

BALDWIN – There is practically no Hospital that I know of, that is not using Light, plain Light or some Colored Lights, in some way and there are great many of our Physicians, who are using Color and Light in their private work. Very few were doing it when Spectro-Chrome was put in evidence.

DINSHAH – Do you remember in Philadelphia, the Jefferson University introducing it recently?

BALDWIN – Well, I know that they do use Light and Color there.

DINSHAH – In Jefferson?

BALDWIN – Yes.

DINSHAH – That is a great University, is it not, don't you know?

BALDWIN – Well, it is one of the best Medical Colleges in the World.

DINSHAH – Now, Doctor, a little more clarification: in the Class work, you heard me playing an Organ?

BALDWIN – Yes.

DINSHAH – What is the purpose of that Organ, in demonstrating what?

BALDWIN – The similarity between or the connection between Sound Waves and Color Waves, Light Waves.

DINSHAH – What is taught by – what is the connection taught, I mean as regards the Oscillatory Frequencies of Sound and so on? Is there any apparatus in the Class or is it by word of mouth only?

BALDWIN – There is an Organ on which you demonstrate Oscillatory Frequencies.

DINSHAH – On the Organ?

BALDWIN – On the Organ.

DINSHAH – The Organ is not for mere entertainment, then; it has a purpose of Oscillatory Frequencies?

BALDWIN – Absolutely.

DINSHAH – How long do I play the Organ, just in the beginning to request the Divine Architect of the Universe to help the work? In the beginning of the Class work, how long do I invoke the Deity's help, by the Organ and a song or a hymn? How long does it take?

BALDWIN – Three to five minutes; I should say, never more than five, perhaps not more than three minutes many times.

DINSHAH – Is the work, according to your viewpoint in a Medical College, conducted along scientific grounds or merely as just a fake system to get money?

BALDWIN – Absolutely most scientific thing there is in the Healing Art today.

DINSHAH – You studied other Courses in Medicine, Surgery and other things?

BALDWIN – I have been through the regular mill.

DINSHAH – Is there any Course that you really can compare in the Science of Spectroscopy, with this Course?

BALDWIN – Not at all.

DINSHAH – In our work, that is?

BALDWIN – Yes, sir.

DINSHAH – Do I show the relation of Chemicals of the Human Body to the Color Waves?

BALDWIN – Yes.

DINSHAH – I offer this People's Exhibit 10 again for you to identify here; the Chemical Chart, as is put there, is step by step experimentally demonstrated with Chemical Tubes and Spectroscopy; this Chart?

BALDWIN – It is.

DINSHAH – And is it found to be just exactly as I teach it or is it merely a fluke, to your mind?

BALDWIN – It is an absolute guide.

DINSHAH – I shall show you a few of these Charts, whether you learned from me. Is this Chart always in my Class Room (indicating and showing to Witness)?

BALDWIN – Yes, sir, practically always.

DINSHAH – You remember it? Learning from it?

BALDWIN – Yes, sir.

JUSTICE – There does not seem to be any dispute about those Charts, Doctor.

DINSIIAII – We shall drop that, Your Honor. I shall save your time, sir. Were you ever to the Spectro-Chrome Institute, at Malaga, New Jersey, the Central Office of this work?

BALDWIN – Yes.

DINSHAH – Is this the place (showing photogram to Witness)?

BALDWIN – I should say it was, yes.

DINSHAH – How many Acres are there? How big is that place?

BALDWIN – You have got 23, about that.

DINSHAH – 23 Acres. How many buildings are there?

BALDWIN – Four or five.

DINSHAH – There is an Auditorium and Research Laboratory there?

BALDWIN – Yes, they are together in one building.

DINSHAH – Resident Quarters?

BALDWIN – Yes, sir.

DINSHAH – Administration Building?

BALDWIN – The Administration Building and the Auditorium is all in one building.

DINSHAH – Printing Plant?

BALDWIN – Printing Plant.

DINSHAH – So that it is not a fly-by-night Institution, according to your mind?

BALDWIN – No.

DINSHAH – But a real Laboratory for serving humanity?

BALDWIN – It is a real Laboratory, sir, serving humanity.

DINSHAH – I shall offer this in Evidence.

(The PHOTOGRAM referred was received in Evidence and marked Defendant's Exhibit 30.)

DINSHAH – You dealt with this Spectro-Chrome Institute for the last 10 years now, nearly?

BALDWIN – Yes, sir.

DINSHAH – In their relations with the public, as you judged from your own experience, how did you find them?

BALDWIN – I have always found them perfectly honest and square, with the intent to do the straight thing.

DINSHAH – Do they fulfill their Contracts?

BALDWIN – Certainly.

DINSHAH – Do they fulfill whatever they tell in the Class Room, as their word of honor?

BALDWIN – Yes, sir.

DINSHAH – Did you ever have any reason to complain against the Institute?

BALDWIN – I have never issued a complaint.

DINSHAH – Was there any reason to issue one?

BALDWIN – If there had been, I certainly should have put it in.

DINSHAH – Thank you. Please take the Witness.

CHAPTER 14

SEALING DOOM OF MEDICINE AND SURGERY

Surgeon Kate W. Baldwin gave such a wonderfully good and true account of Spectro-Chrome Metry, that Prosecutor Leo Hagerty must have formed a slightly different opinion of the Defendant than he had before. He must have wiggled in his chair often at the sledgehammer replies of the esteemed Doctor, but he jumped to his feet nevertheless, to do something to break down her Testimony. [See the Addendum for four photos pertaining to the following dialogue.]

HAGERTY – Doctor, isn't the use of waxed paper or paraffin recognized as the standard treatment of Burns?

BALDWIN – Yes, but naturally there is no paraffin or wax left in the paper after it has been sterilized.

HAGERTY – But the use of waxed paper or paraffin is recognized as a standard treatment of Burns?

BALDWIN – Paraffin is, yes, paraffin is sprayed over the parts very many times, but there was no paraffin or wax left in the paper; it was all taken out by the cloth; there was one layer of cloth and also of paper and put in a Sterilizer; there was not a bit of wax left in it.

HAGERTY – You mean, when this girl's picture was taken here, she was treated, instead of following the usual procedure or following the standard treatment of Burns, by using wax paper or paraffin that the paper was treated so that the paraffin or wax was taken out of the paper?

BALDWIN – Yes, sir.

HAGERTY – Did you then use an absolutely radical change from what was recognized the standard treatment?

BALDWIN – I had been in the habit of using thin silk for a long time, but, silk was most too expensive for an extensive thing like that.

HAGERTY – What I am getting at is, in this

particular case that you have spoken of as far as you knew, upto that time, one of these standard – at least one of the standard treatments of Burns was the use of waxed paper, then in the treatment of this case, that standard treatment was departed from entirely by taking the wax out of the paper?

BALDWIN – By taking the wax out of the paper; the standard treatment there with the wax was more to spray it on in some way than it was to just use a waxed paper to put on.

HAGERTY – Was the nature of this girl's Burn, Doctor, was it primary or – what was the –

BALDWIN – You mean whether it was first, second or third degree Burn?

HAGERTY – Yes.

BALDWIN – It was a Burn from fire. Her clothes caught afire and it was all the grades in different parts, from the first degree to the third degree Burn.

HAGERTY – If too much damage has not been done by a Burn and this standard treatment of waxed paper or paraffin, spraying of the paraffin is used, it would effect a complete cure, would it not?

BALDWIN – Just state that again.

HAGERTY – If, in a case of Burn, where the damage was not too extensive, what I mean by that, not too –

BALDWIN – All are the third degree Burns, yes. I understand what you mean.

HAGERTY – I do not mean in Area, if not damaged too much, this standard treatment of waxed paper or paraffin would effect a complete cure, would it not?

BALDWIN – In some cases it would, yes, but, there are other cases that are so damaged that is when we know the paraffin was not taken up by every Surgeon by any means.

HAGERTY – And this covering of this girl's Body with this paper, which you have described was continued, was it, during the course of her convalescence?

BALDWIN – Yes, sir.

HAGERTY – And she was put on a diet, in other words, to build her System up and so forth.

BALDWIN – To build her System up. In a general way, yes, we looked after the Elimination and the building up diet.

HAGERTY – How long after she came inside the Hospital, was the Spectro-Chrome used or this Spectro-Chrome started?

BALDWIN – About two hours.

HAGERTY – Two hours after she came in the Hospital?

BALDWIN – She still was having the effect of the Burn itself, that is, the stinging burning, so forth, so we put her immediately on Spectro-Chrome to overcome that.

HAGERTY – The cause of death from a Burn like that – what is the direct cause of death?

BALDWIN – Well, it is usually a lack of Elimination through the Skin, the functioning of the Skin and the Kidneys are very apt to go off.

HAGERTY – It is some kind of a poisoning developed?

BALDWIN – It is some kind of a poisoning developed; there is no way of eliminating the Poison; we eliminate a great deal of the Poison through the Skin and the Kidneys and the Bowels and the Lungs.

JUSTICE – Comes out through this process of Perspiration?

BALDWIN – Yes.

HAGERTY – What kind of poisoning do you call that? Is that Uremic?

BALDWIN – Well, there is no special name for it, as I know of; it is a toxic condition; depends a good deal upon what was in the – you get a toxic condition from the Tissues that are being thrown off; whatever condition the patient may be in, would determine to a great extent what Toxin it would throw off.

HAGERTY – So that a person's recovery from a Burn, depends a whole lot upon the Elimination?

BALDWIN – A whole lot upon the Elimination, yes.

HAGERTY – And if the Poison which has developed can be eliminated in various ways, through the Bowels and so forth, their chances of recovery are so much better?

BALDWIN – Certainly.

HAGERTY – How old was this child, this girl?

BALDWIN – Eight years old.

HAGERTY – So that the probabilities are that her physical condition and her process of Elimination were in very good condition, were they not?

BALDWIN – Very good, yes. She was not a child that had been properly fed or brought up at all; she was the middle one of seven children, with but enough money to take care of two.

HAGERTY – Are you a Member of the American Medical Association?

BALDWIN – Yes, sir.

HAGERTY – And do you know whether this Jefferson Hospital is a Chartered University?

BALDWIN – Oh, yes. It is one of the oldest Medical Schools in the Country.

JUSTICE – Is that connected with the University of Pennsylvania?

BALDWIN – No, sir, it is a separate institution entirely.

HAGERTY – Have you abandoned the practice of Medicine?

BALDWIN – No, I have not abandoned it. I use it if I have to, but I shall not use it as long as I can get Spectro-Chrome; if I was cut out somewhere where I could not get Spectro-Chrome, I would have to go back to the next best thing.

HAGERTY – You apparently have been convinced, through the teachings of the Colonel and other things, that Spectro-Chrome surpasses Medicine?

BALDWIN – I have.

HAGERTY – So that in your mind, you practically have abandoned the practice of Medicine?

BALDWIN – Only if in a matter of emergency that I would use the old methods of treatment.

HAGERTY – How long have you been in that frame of mind?

BALDWIN – Well, I commenced to use Spectro-Chrome the latter part of 1920 or first of 1921 and it did not take me very long to decide that it was better than anything else I had.

HAGERTY – And then, if I understand your Testimony correctly, you are of the opinion too, that Spectro-Chrome will cure anything and everything?

BALDWIN – No, there was not anything on the face of the Earth that will cure anything and everything. We have all of us got to die some time.

HAGERTY – Well, of course, I do not mean that. There is always a time when we are going to die; I am going to die; you are going to die, I suppose. What I mean, Doctor, is that it will cure any of the so-called Diseases?

BALDWIN – Any of the so-called Diseases, anything that is reasonably curable, it will cure and it will cure many things which Drugs and General Surgery and surgical work will not and surgical work will do better – cases of Surgery will do better, if you use Spectro-Chrome in connection with it, than if you use only the old surgical method.

HAGERTY – It will cure Dementia Praecox, will it?

BALDWIN – Other people have had those cases and cured them. I have not had a case of that brought in.

HAGERTY – Would you cure the Dementia Praecox then, before you found out that –

BALDWIN – I never had a case of it in my whole practice.

HAGERTY – You never had a case of that in your whole practice?

BALDWIN – No.

HAGERTY – Did you study it?

BALDWIN – Yes.

HAGERTY – It is a mental Disease, is it not?

BALDWIN – Yes, we had a general Course in Mental Diseases.

HAGERTY – Was there a cure for it, before Spectro-Chrome could cure it, do you know?

BALDWIN – Well, there was never any definite cure for it; some would use one method and some would use another; good many cases were cured and some cases were not cured.

JUSTICE – It is generally recognized as incurable, is it?

BALDWIN – Permanently incurable.

HAGERTY – That is, as far as the medical profession has been concerned, it was recognized as incurable, either by Surgery or by Medicine, Drugs?

BALDWIN – Yes.

HAGERTY – But you know of cases that have been cured by Spectro-Chrome?

BALDWIN – Not personally.

HAGERTY – I mean, you have not treated them personally, but you have –

BALDWIN – I have heard people say that they have –

DINSHAH – Your Honor, hearsay Evidence can not be admitted.

JUSTICE – Well, it is helping you.

DINSHAH – Yes, even then, I am fair to the other party too. We shall stick to the Law; your own personal experience.

JUSTICE – I think the Colonel is right.

HAGERTY – It will cure any Venereal Disease?

BALDWIN – It, in my hands, has cured Gonorrhea and Syphilis.

HAGERTY – Syphilis?

BALDWIN – Yes, sir.

HAGERTY – As far as the medical profession is concerned, Syphilis, when it reaches a certain stage, was generally recognized as incurable, was it not?

BALDWIN – No, not now. We can usually find something in the regular medical work, Surgery, that will eventually heal the destructive process.

HAGERTY – It will stop it?

BALDWIN – It will stop it, yes.

HAGERTY – It will stop the Disease, but it won't cure it?

BALDWIN – Well, you can get it so that the general tests for the Disease are negative.

HAGERTY – Will Spectro-Chrome cure Tuberculosis.

BALDWIN – Yes, sir.

HAGERTY – And will it cure Cancer?

BALDWIN – In many cases of Cancer, it will, if there has not been too much destruction of Tissue, Spectro-Chrome will cure it, will build up the Tissue. If it has to come to Operation and there is a great deal of destruction of Tissue it will simply make them comfortable for the rest of their lives, but it will make them comfortable so that they can enjoy the rest of their life to a certain extent, without doping them with Opiates.

HAGERTY – There are great many World recognized Physicians who are attempting to find a cure for Cancer, are there not?

BALDWIN – Yes, it is one of the hard things that the Medical World is trying to do and they have not gotten very far with it.

HAGERTY – But Spectro-Chrome will cure it?

BALDWIN – I say Spectro-Chrome with – not an advanced case will cure it, on the surface like the Epithelium; I have had a number of those that were cured.

HAGERTY – And the Medical World has always been looking for a cure for Tuberculosis too, has it not?

BALDWIN – Yes.

HAGERTY – But, Spectro-Chrome will cure Tuberculosis?

BALDWIN – Do you wish a case cited as –

HAGERTY – No, I do not care about going into specific cases. I am just asking your opinion about Spectro-Chrome. That is what I am getting at.

BALDWIN – It has done it, in cases where there were big Festers and small Festers, where it had been pronounced advanced cases and was ready for the Sanatarium, to go into the advanced wards and I have had patients that had been in bed most of the time for three or four years and had been in the Sanatarium part

of that time, who came under Spectro-Chrome and there is one case now who is back in the Sanatorium now nursing, because she says she feels that people who have had Tuberculosis and gotten over it, are the ones who should take care of the tubercular people.

HAGERTY – Do you believe in the use of Surgery, any more Doctor?

BALDWIN – In some cases, yes; Surgery, Constructive Surgery, is necessary in certain cases.

HAGERTY – Do you believe in any general theory that Spectro-Chrome can take the place of Surgery and leave organs with a person that would – perhaps, Cancer be taken out by Surgeon?

BALDWIN – Oh, yes! I have had Strangulated Hernia that had been taken care of by Spectro-Chrome and no further Operation. I have had ordinary Hernias. The Muscles tone up so, that they needed no Operation and no Trusses and many of those things; but I actually had people brought to me that were billed for the Operating Table in a few hours and have been taken out of the Hospital and brought to my Office with Appendicitis; they have been wheeled in and have not had their Appendix out. I have had various Appendix cases, that have been diagnosed Appendicitis and advised to have Operation, that have never had any Operation.

HAGERTY – Will it cure Appendicitis and Hernia too?

BALDWIN – Yes.

HAGERTY – Besides the other Diseases that you have spoken about?

BALDWIN – Yes, sir.

HAGERTY – When a patient comes to you, you diagnose the case, do you not?

BALDWIN – Well, you know, if you have been using and doing a thing, you can not help using the knowledge that you have gained over years of experience. I am not limited, of course, as the layman is, in connection with Spectro-Chrome.

HAGERTY – Well, that is what I am getting at.

BALDWIN – I could use only – if it was possible for me to eliminate all my previous knowledge I could do practically as good work as I do now, with Spectro-Chrome.

HAGERTY – Well, then, do you recognize Colonel Dinshah's teachings that Diagnosis is entirely unnecessary?

BALDWIN – Well, Diagnosis from the medical standpoint, yes.

HAGERTY – In other words that you join with him in his teachings, that, for instance, it docs not make any difference whether a person is suffering from Typhoid Fever or Scarlet Fever or any other Fever, that it is all a Fever and are treated by certain Light?

BALDWIN – Any toxic, any septic condition, is practically the same thing.

HAGERTY – Well, you do not, I suppose, believe in that part of the teaching of Colonel Dinshah, do you?

BALDWIN – Well, I think that we treated – most people treat Fevers and things to a great extent in the same way.

HAGERTY – That is, they treat Scarlet Fever, the same as Typhoid Fever?

BALDWIN – To a great extent by keeping up the Elimination and feeding them properly and all that sort of thing, as any layman knows.

HAGERTY – Do you agree then that it does not make any difference, really whether the person's Disease like, say Tuberculosis whether it is in the incipient stage or in the advanced stage?

BALDWIN – Well, of course, you can get results quicker in incipient stage than you can in the advanced stage.

HAGERTY – But as far as the treatment is concerned, it is the same then?

BALDWIN – As far as the treatment is concerned not exactly just the same because an advanced case the Cavities fill with Pus there are Cavities as big as that (indicating) in the Apex, 2/3 filled with Pus or lots of small Cavities through the Lung, that absolutely had been healed entirely.

HAGERTY – With Spectro-Chrome?

BALDWIN – According to X-Rays.

HAGERTY – You are not connected with any Hospital now, Doctor?

BALDWIN – I am not, at the present time, no.

HAGERTY – How long since?

BALDWIN – Three years.

HAGERTY – You say you have got 10 of these Machines working. Where are they working?

BALDWIN – Where are they working?

HAGERTY – Yes.

BALDWIN – Well, my Office is 1117 Spruce Street and I have the different Treatment Rooms fixed up there.

HAGERTY – That is, you have your Office with different rooms and a Machine in each room?

BALDWIN – Yes or two or three Machines; that is, they are similar Machines. In good many of the Treatment Rooms – I have two Machines, for two different places of the Body at the same time, to save their time and my time too.

HAGERTY – But persons who can not come to your Office, you install Machines in their home?

BALDWIN – Occasionally. I do not do much outside work; I have not time for outside work, in fact, turn down most of the outside work. It seems necessary to come to my Office once or twice a week and if I feel they need oftener treatments, I let them take a Machine, to use at their home between times.

HAGERTY – You say it is your opinion and your frank and sincere opinion, after you have told us about all the experience you have had in Medicine, 41 years of general practice and Surgery in Hospitals and so forth, that if you did not have that practice and knowledge, that you could obtain the same results with this Machine?

BALDWIN – If I used all the instruments and the Diagnostic Instrument that the Colonel has given, I think I could get practically the same results.

HAGERTY – I do not quite understand when you say "Diagnostic Instrument". I thought there was no Diagnosis.

BALDWIN – Well, the Medical Profession would call them Diagnostic Instruments. They are given Instruments which will tell you whether your one place of the Body is too cold and the other too hot; one place of the Body is feeble and the other is overstimulated, whether you have a Fever or whether you do not have a Fever. In reality, you know your different Organs are made up of different Chemical Elements; your Liver has not the same Chemical Elements as your Spleen.

HAGERTY – Then part of it there, anyhow, of this Apparatus here, you have certain Instruments with which you make some kind of a Diagnosis?

BALDWIN – Well, if you call it Diagnosis, if you wish; the lay people are taught not to use the term "Diagnosis".

JUSTICE – That is, because a Rose by any other name –

BALDWIN – By any other name, will be just the same, Judge, exactly.

HAGERTY – In other words, the Colonel, in teaching lay people, wants to see that they protect themselves?

BALDWIN – So that they do not get in wrong with the Law.

HAGERTY – Prevents the Practice of Medicine without a License ?

DINSHAH – I object to that question. Nobody is brought here for any Violation of the Law, Your Honor.

JUSTICE – I take it that she does not know what the Colonel thinks.

DINSHAH – That is the idea.

JUSTICE – So I sustain that Objection.

HAGERTY – That is, you say the Colonel teaches his lay patients – I suppose the lay patients are any patients who might come, wish to get interested, is that it?

BALDWIN – Yes. I think, the Colonel, if he saw that somebody was entirely unfitted for the work, he would counsel them to not take the Course. I do not think he would ever accept a person in his Class that he felt was unfitted to take the work, simply for the Hundred Dollars or whatever his charge.

HAGERTY – In other words, your opinion of the Colonel is, that if somebody came up and undertook this Course and paid him One Hundred Fifty Dollars for it and if he found out that he was an entirely unqualified, why, he would not take the money?

BALDWIN – He would say: "Take your $150 back; you are not fitted for this work".

HAGERTY – For instance, if a man has no more qualifications for a Course than say, repairing Washing Machines, Lawn Mowers and so forth, you believe that if the Colonel knew that, he would give him his money back and tell him not to take the Course?

BALDWIN – There is many a person with good common sense, where good common sense goes further than lots of technical knowledge and he may be a man that is doing Washing Machine repairing and Lawn Mowers, that would have more common sense to bring into his use, than some college – Medical College Graduates have.

HAGERTY – I did not mean that in criticizing anybody's education.

BALDWIN – Well, his education is the general education, his general, common sense and ability to take things in, whether he has had a technical education or not, seems to me, counts quite a good ways.

HAGERTY – You mean, Doctor, that supposing a person has no knowledge whatever of Anatomy or has no knowledge at all of Chem-icals or of the Sun's Rays, any technical knowledge of that, has never done anything during their life about these, leaving out their education, they may be a person of common sense and that by handling some kind of a Machine, do you believe that then, that person could come and take a Lecture – a Course of Lectures – sixty hours – and at the end of sixty hours of Lecture, talking as the Colonel does and as you heard him, talking fast about Chemistry and Chemical Elements and all these names, that if he then put in the sixty hours of that time, that that person could then take that Apparatus and get results from it?

BALDWIN – I think they could, if they used all the Apparatus that he has given for finding out what the trouble is,

HAGERTY – And that the results would be the same, those results could be obtained for persons suffering from Dementia Praecox or a Venereal Disease or Cancer or Tuberculosis or Ulcers of the Stomach or any of those things?

BALDWIN – If they use the means that is given them and stick strictly to what they are told to do by Colonel Dinshah, I think they would come out with a larger percentage of benefits than the average Medical Doctor does.

HAGERTY – Oh, then, if I understand you, then, you think that a person under those circumstances, would be better equipped to do this, than the average Medical Doctor?

BALDWIN – I think he would be better equipped after the one Course than the ordinary Doctor is, when he or she comes out of Medical College. You know mighty little, you know, of the Human Body, when you come out; you have got a lot of technical work, a lot of technical terms, you can give all the Bones of the Body and the Muscles and all their attachments, but you have not any knowledge of a Human Being, so to speak and your Sympathetic Nervous System and your Occult System, your real self aside from your Physical Body, is of more importance than your actual Bones and Muscles are.

HAGERTY – Well, you mean that the Medical Student who has, as l understand it, spent several years of studying the Body and Anatomy and so forth, that when he comes out and also has to serve an Internship in the Hospital, does he not, before he is admitted to practice?

BALDWIN – In most of the States, they are obliged to.

HAGERTY – So that, how many years, for instance, in Pennsylvania does a young man have to study and then serve an Internship and so forth, before he is admitted to practice?

BALDWIN – Well, it is pretty well towards six years before he will get into practice.

HAGERTY – Well, I thought six or seven years here?

BALDWIN – About that time.

HAGERTY – But you believe that the average person who would go and attend one of Colonel Dinshah's Course of Lectures of 60 hours and graduate and get one of these Diplomas, would be better fitted, better equipped to get results than the Medical Student who has gone through these Courses and Internship?

BALDWIN – A Medical Student nowadays, when he comes out of college, depends almost 95 per cent. for his ability to do anything, because of the Laboratories with which he is associated; everything is sent to the Laboratory; Medical Students are not taught to make outside Diagnosis anymore; they really have to depend upon a Laboratory Report, for practically everything that they do.

HAGERTY – Well, that is in an effort to get the medical profession to make –

BALDWIN – To complicate things.

HAGERTY – Make the Diagnosis more certain?

BALDWIN – Well, I suppose it does. It complicates matters very much.

HAGERTY – But in this Spectro-Chrome, Diagnosis, it is not necessary, is it?

BALDWIN – Not what – we do not call it Diagnosis. You are going to find out whether the person is below par or above par, whether he is on the Fever Side or the Cold Side and that is all that Medicine does.

HAGERTY – Did Colonel Dinshah, in the course of his teachings, at the various times you have been there, did he tell you that the Machine itself diagnoses the case?

BALDWIN – No, sir. That Machine does not diagnose anything.

HAGERTY – Well, from what I understand, Doctor, from you –

BALDWIN – Does not tell you anything, as to what to do either; the Machine does not,

HAGERTY – I understand, from the way you testified here, you have very definitely turned your back on Medicine?

BALDWIN – I have. I would close my Office tonight never to see another sick person, unless it was an emergency, if I had to go back to old style Medicine and give up Spectro-Chrome. Now, that is just honest – that just represents my belief in Spectro-Chrome.

HAGERTY – Well, that is what I mean. So that you have been completely sold on Spectro-Chrome?

BALDWIN – I am completely sold on Spectro-Chrome and I gave no case in which I had not personally had experience.

HAGERTY – That is all.

The curtain of Cross Examination descended at this juncture. The Witness came out of the grill, untouched by all the quirks and twists that the Prosecutor could design – the day of Medicine passed forever. A great Senior Surgeon – a woman whose medical and surgical practice in Clinical and Hospital services extended over two score years, had spoken in all honesty, from varied personal experience – sealed the doom of Poison, Puspunching and Poniard Therapy.

CHAPTER 15
SPECTRO-CHROME SAFE WITHOUT DIAGNOSIS

After Prosecutor Leo Hagerty finished, it was the Defendant's turn to untangle the knots and he promptly started.

DINSHAH – Please, just a little clarification of the points involved, Dr. Baldwin, so as not to leave anything, You spoke about the Sympathetic Nervous System and so on. I shall show you a Chart issued by the Institute, People's Exhibit Number 11. Do you recognize this so-called complicated Chart, with foreign words, so forth and so on?

BALDWIN – I do, yes.

DINSHAH – Is this a part of the Course?

BALDWIN – Yes.

DINSHAH – What kind of part does it take in this work?

BALDWIN – Well, it goes into the part where the Sympathetic Nervous System is involved.

DINSHAH – Is the Sympathetic Nervous System one of the great things that regulates the functions of the Human Body?

BALDWIN – The Sympathetic Nervous System regulates all of the Automatic Functions of the Body.

DINSHAH – That is what is known as the Autonomous Nervous System?

BALDWIN – Yes, your Heart keeps on beating, you keep on breathing, your nutrition goes on, all of things go on through the action of the Sympathetic Nervous System.

DINSHAH – Is this work shown by me, directly stated in the Class, by my own self to the Students, exemplifying that term just as demonstrated?

BALDWIN – Yes.

DINSHAH – It is.

BALDWIN – Yes.

DINSHAH – Did you ever find any fault in practical work, in your own clinical work, when you applied this work?

BALDWIN – I have not.

DINSHAH – You use it every day in your work?

BALDWIN – I use it everyday; that is, certain parts of it; I do not go into all of this Sanskrit.

DINSHAH – But, the American phraseology is beneath to explain it?

BALDWIN – The American phraseology I go into.

DINSHAH – This is a genuine Science there?

BALDWIN – A genuine Science.

DINSHAH – And you apply it in your daily work?

BALDWIN – I do.

DINSHAH – Now, there is some confusion about this Constructive Surgery and Destructive Surgery. I want to qualify that. Does Spectro-Chrome Institute, through my mouth, ever teach that Surgery as applied to the Human Body to build up a broken Bone or anything, is useless?

BALDWIN – No. You always have said that outside of Constructive Surgery –

DINSHAH – When the Institute says, "No Surgery", it simply means "No Destructive Surgery"?

BALDWIN – No Destructive Surgery.

DINSHAH – That is, the Human Body is like a Machine; if a part of the Machine inside can be saved, save it by Spectro-Chrome if you can, but do not let it be cut off?

BALDWIN – Unless you can not save it.

DINSHAH – That means, then, to clear the situation in ordinary language, if a woman is sick from any Disorder, according to our System, in 60 hours anyone ought to be able to tonate and give service, if we find that part out of equilibrium, that we have the means of repairing that damage and save that part from being taken out?

BALDWIN – In the large proportion of cases, yes.

DINSHAH – And did you do that with Spectro-Chrome?

BALDWIN – I have.

DINSHAH – In Constructive Surgery then, Spectro-Chrome leads over any other system?

BALDWIN – In Constructive Surgery, yes and in all other Surgery, it will do better, you will get better results if you use Spectro-Chrome in connection with your other Surgery, than you will if you trust to your Surgery.

DINSHAH – Supposing you had a broken Bone – somebody comes with the Femur broken or any part – any Bone broken and after the Surgeon has performed the mechanical work of putting the Bones together, what is the idea of Spectro-Chrome?

BALDWIN – In tonating and setting into equilibrium those Disorders there. In the first place, you can get a general Systemic condition; in another, you can get better Nutrition and Elimination and all of that will be good and that will help to build the Bone, help to nourish the whole Body; you have got to pay attention to the whole Body. Then, in many times, in broken Bones, Nature has not sufficient power to throw out Callus and there Callus is similar to mending Tissue that is thrown out between the ends of the broken Bones and in thick Bones, it runs up in, we get a Bone Callus or get an intermediate Callus, a Callus that holds it; many times there is not vitality enough to any of that Callus thrown out. If we use Spectro-Chrome on that, we will produce the necessary Stimulation and the Callus will be thrown out. In other conditions, there is an excess of Callus, which occasions a mean deformity.

DINSHAH – Now, Doctor, in this case where it is compulsory, you have to take on the Operating Table, for instance, a Foot that is reduced to a pulp by an automobile truck going on it, which can not be set right, when you must perform a compulsory Surgical Operation to remove it, you have found Spectro-Chrome even in those cases, useful during the process, when you gave gas for an Anesthesia?

BALDWIN – Well, Spectro-Chrome before Anesthesia, you mean?

DINSHAH – Yes.

BALDWIN – It makes the Anesthetic very much more quietly taken, if you can give the proper Spectro-Chrome, before you send the patient to the Operating Table, they will take the Anesthesia much more quietly and they will recover from it with much less unpleasantness in the way of Nausea and Vomiting and so forth.

DINSHAH – About this Diagnosis which has been put in by the learned Counsellor, I want to ask you one question: Is Medical Diagnosis a hundred percent correct?

BALDWIN – It is not claimed to be a hundred percent.

DINSHAH – What is the correct percentage?

BALDWIN – The percentage is about from 50 to 52 percent.

DINSHAH – 52 correct?

BALDWIN – Yes.

DINSHAH – That means that if a person simply adheres to Medical and Surgical Diagnosis, 48 percent of the people would be ripped open for something they did not have for which to be ripped open?

BALDWIN – I am afraid I will have to admit that. I am sorry.

DINSHAH – And in Spectro-Chrome, while it does not deal with differential diagnostic names of Disorders, is there any chance of a person putting the Spectro-Chrome wrongly and damaging the System?

BALDWIN – No, sir.

DINSHAH – Therefore, what is your opinion of Spectro-Chrome, from the standpoint of safety to the public?

BALDWIN – Absolutely. I think I might say, absolutely you can do no real harm with Spectro-Chrome.

DINSHAH – There was a medical gentleman here, who spoke about some Lights, which if put on the Eye for an hour would burn it. If that Spectro-Chrome thousand-Watt Bulb that is there, be put with that Indigo Color Slide, made by Violet and Blue together and the Eye be put right into the Focus of that for an hour, what effect would happen?

BALDWIN – There would be no harm done.

DINSHAH – Can any harm be done to the most delicate Eye by Spectro-Chrome?

BALDWIN – No, I should say not, from the number of cases I have used it in, directly.

DINSHAH – You had six of those Eye cases?

BALDWIN – Of those cases – case came in when the trouble was with the Eye, swollen; absolutely used Indigo.

DINSHAH – Something has been said by you about people diagnosing and "Diagnostic Machine". You do not see a Diagnostic Machine on Exhibit, on the floor there with this Instrument?

BALDWIN – It is not here.

DINSHAH – You have one of my so-called "Finding Machine" or Itisometer?

BALDWIN – Yes, sir.

DINSHAH – Is this the Chart of that, Exhibit Number, Complainant's Number eight?

BALDWIN – Yes, sir.

DINSHAH – You use this Chart daily in your work?

BALDWIN – Yes, sir.

DINSHAH – And by means of that Machine and this Chart, what do you determine without using your Head altogether, medically, diagnostically or in any manner, what does that Machine do for you with the Equipment?

BALDWIN – It only tells me what to do for the patient.

DINSHAH – That means, that that is entirely in the machine made by me, which is not on exhibit here, for which this Chart is given and taught in the Class to use that Equipment?

BALDWIN – Yes.

DINSHAH – And if I tell you that that Machine is made for those, who do not want to use their Head even with that Equipment – that is **my** Head in that Machine! Is that right?

BALDWIN – That is quite right.

DINSHAH – And the name of that Machine is the Itisometer?

BALDWIN – Yes, sir.

DINSHAH – It does not do any diagnostic work according to Medicine or Surgery?

BALDWIN – No.

DINSHAH – That has only to do with that Equipment and Color Slides?

BALDWIN – Yes, sir.

DINSHAH – Only that?

BALDWIN – Only that.

DINSHAH – Is it an absolute necessity that that Machine should be used?

BALDWIN – To do good work, I should say it is, particularly with the layman. I think that every layman doing work with Color, should use it.

DINSHAH – But a man who is not able to spend so much money and does not want to go and serve to that extent, with that Equipment and the 60 hours' knowledge gained in the Class, is he able to serve the public with safety?

BALDWIN – Yes, with safety. Under those circumstances, I would say he had better confine himself to his own family, though.

DINSHAH – All right. No questions, Your Honor.

Here Surgeon Kate W. Baldwin's Re-Cross Examination began.

CHAPTER 16
ITISOMETER, DELICATE AND ACCURATE

Prosecutor Leo Hagerty could not sit quiet, when he heard the sand piles he had erected crumble. So he started again to get some advantage.

HAGERTY – What kind of a Machine is this "Finding Machine", Doctor Baldwin?

BALDWIN – This? That Machine (indicating)?

HAGERTY – Yes, the Finding Machine that is?

BALDWIN – Why, it is a Machine that is made by Colonel Dinshah, a very delicate, accurate Machine which shows you the amount of deviation from the normal that there is.

HAGERTY – So that then, the person really does not have to be qualified in your method, if he has got that?

BALDWIN – If he has got that Machine and will follow it, in 99 cases out of 100, he will do good.

HAGERTY – So that if a person has this – what do you call it? Itisometer?

BALDWIN – Itisometer.

HAGERTY – And will apply the Itisometer, the Itisometer will tell him what is –

BALDWIN – What the Color should be.

HAGERTY – What is wrong with the person and what the Colors will be to use?

BALDWIN – Yes.

HAGERTY – So that it is really an automatic process, then?

BALDWIN – It is an automatic process; I must say it is automatic; it would be as good a term as any.

The Prosecutor was getting into a deeper hole each time he tried to crack through this Surgeon's Testimony; so he sat down and the Defendant entered into Re-Re-Direct Examination of the Witness.

DINSHAH – That Machine is a patented Machine, is it not?

BALDWIN – Yes.

DINSHAH – Here is the Patent (indicating). Your Honor can take Judicial Notice of it.

JUSTICE – Of which Machine is this?

DINSHAH – The Itisometer. (To Witness) Is this the Dial of the Machine that you are using? The Main Dial and the Auriculator and other parts? I do not want to go into the issues. Is this part of it?

BALDWIN – That is the diagram.

DINSHAH – And does this represent the inside of it, as you saw it in the Class Room many times or in the Laboratory?

BALDWIN – I have never seen the inside of the Machine.

DINSHAH – But it is the Dial System?

BALDWIN – Yes.

DINSHAH – And it is an Electric Thermometer in fact, showing which Organ is affected?

BALDWIN – That is just about it.

DINSHAH – And in the Class I showed that this Instrument is sensitive to 1/40th of a Degree Fahrenheit, for detecting difference in the Circulation and so on? Is that right?

BALDWIN – Yes.

DINSHAH – I offer that Patent, Number 1,724,469, granted by the United States Government, August 13, 1929, in Exhibit.

(The PATENT referred was received in Evidence and marked Defendant's Exhibit 31.)

DINSHAH – You use this in your daily practice, to avoid using any scientific Diagnosis?

BALDWIN – It is so much more exact than anything else, that it is wise to use it.

DINSHAH – That is all.

But that was not all. The Prosecutor believed he could still tackle the learned Surgeon and get from her some point that would help The People of the State of New York. So, he started the grinding mill.

HAGERTY – Did you ever hear of Palmer's Machine in Chiropractic?

BALDWIN – I know of it. I have never used it. I have seen it demonstrated.

HAGERTY – Is there any difference between them?

BALDWIN – Oh, yes, very great difference between them.

HAGERTY – Between it and Palmer's Machine in Chiropractic.

DINSHAH – She says she has not seen it.

BALDWIN – I beg your pardon. I have seen it. I said I have never used it.

HAGERTY – It is not in any way similar to the Itisometer?

BALDWIN – I don't know. There may be some similarity somewhere about it. I have not gone into the technicalities of that Machine to the extent of saying that there was no similarity.

The Prosecutor sat down and more Examination commenced from the Defendant.

DINSHAH – Dr. Palmer's Machine and the Palmer System, have nothing to do with Color Waves?

BALDWIN – No.

DINSHAH – It is only Chiropractic?

BALDWIN – It is only Chiropractic.

DINSHAH – Our System has nothing to do with Chiropractic in any manner?

BALDWIN – Not at all.

DINSHAH – We use no Manipulation?

BALDWIN – No.

DINSHAH – No Drugs?

BALDWIN – No.

DINSHAH – No Differential Diagnosis or Surgery in our work?

BALDWIN – No, sir.

DINSHAH – No questions.

The Defendant then requested to call for Howard Page.

JUSTICE – Is he a Doctor?

DINSHAH – He is a man who was given service by Spectro-Chrome Metry. Do you want me to get only medical people on it?

JUSTICE – I think that is the only one that is competent. So many other factors enter into it. You can see my reason.

DINSHAH – I see your reasons. We shall save time.

JUSTICE – The Doctors are competent Witnesses.

DINSHAH – Will not my lay Graduates also be competent Witnesses, from the standpoint of Spectro-Chrome?

JUSTICE – I am afraid not, Doctor.

DINSHAH – Of the Spectro-Chrome?

JUSTICE – No; I am afraid not.

The Defendant bowed to the opinion of the Court, and Dr. Kate W. Baldwin left the stand. Her Testimony stayed unshaken.

* * * * *

10. The testimony of Dinshah's next witness, Dr. Martha J. Peebles, was somewhat similar to that of Dr. Baldwin in that she was a highly experienced professional, and completely dedicated to Spectro-Chrome. She was a Medical Inspector in the Brooklyn NY Department of Health; was a front line Army Company surgeon; became an invalid from arthritis and neuritis, met Dr. Baldwin and according to her sworn testimony, cured herself of these diseases with Spectro-Chrome and in one month resumed her private practice. She eventually employed 17 equipments (presently called projectors) on a daily basis for such conditions as tumors, sciatica, heart disorders, meningitis, goiter, ulcers, thrombosis, neuritis, and many other disorders. Her testimony also covered numerous technical points as taught by Dinshah in his classes.

11. The concluding phase of Dinshah's defense was the evidence from two of his Graduate non-medical (lay) practitioners, Bessie A. Hasenau and Jessie E. Ness; and a non-practicing Graduate, Bessie Radcliffe. They substantiated his assertion that using Spectro-Chrome successfully did not require extensive medical training.

12. The defense presentation must have been considerably more robust than the prosecutor had anticipated. He now summoned a rebuttal witness, an authority on analytic chemistry and with other qualifications, Dr. Albert P. Sy. His statements were in essence the same as those of the scientist earlier in the case, that while Light is essential to life for obvious reasons, various frequencies (Colors) cause no noticeable biologic effects on higher organisms. It is, of course, now widely recognized that humans are affected by the type of Light we use as well as by its intensity and duration. One example is now termed "seasonal affective disorder" (SAD).

13. Dinshah and Dr. Sy made a great pair: They were both very well educated, though on opposite sides of the legal fence. Dinshah deftly fenced, thrusting and

parrying, to get Dr. Sy to admit some points essential to the <u>defense</u>. This was the usual tactical move made by Dinshah in fighting lawsuits, using prosecution witnesses for his own purposes to a level where sometimes it was difficult to distinguish whether the witness he was cross-examining was for the prosecution or for the defense.

14.   The final scene in a trial consists of a summation of the facts as seen by the defense, and then by the prosecutor, finishing with the charge to the jury by the judge.   New York State Supreme Court Justice Thomas H. Noonan gave the jury a carefully worded overview of the case.   There were of course the legal aspects, but in one paragraph he concisely covered the real issue before the jury, "The gist of this lawsuit is, that according to the People's claim, the Doctor [Dinshah] misrepresented the healing capacity or power of this machine.   That is, they claim it can not do anywhere near what the Doctor is alleged to have claimed it would do.   If this machine is a useful machine and can do good, practical results, in the cure of disease, then, I take it your verdict should be 'Not Guilty'."   The jury deliberated for only 90 minutes before returning to the courtroom with their unanimous verdict: **NOT GUILTY** on all counts of the indictment.   They apparently felt that Spectro-Chrome indeed "can do good, practical results, in the cure of disease."

15.   That was the successful conclusion of the Buffalo NY ordeal but it was far from the end of the tribulations for Dinshah.   In the following 17 years he fought seven more lawsuits of varying significance the last of which was followed by an insurmountable permanent interstate injunction in 1957.   The Forces of Ignorance had accomplished their aim at last; or had they?   Dinshah continued, limited by the injunction to sales in New Jersey, until his death in 1966.   At that point, three of his sons who had been raised in service to the Spectro-Chrome Institutes, assumed responsibility for advancing the use of Spectro-Chrome and in 1975 founded the non-profit Dinshah Health Society.

16.   In the past ten to twenty years there has been a considerable change in many people's mind-set regarding orthodox medicine.   The US Federal government now has an Office of Alternative Medicine and sees fit (as of 1994) to list this Society as an information source; this of course does not constitute an endorsement but at least it shows an open mind.

17.   Though much has changed, much has remained the same.   There is still rigid control of medical devices so it will take some effort on your part to assemble the necessary material for a Spectro-Chrome equipment since we can not sell them or their parts.   There are suggestions in previous Chapters for Light sources and filters, and Chapter 14 shows how to make a simple, efficient projector.   So, isn't it time you found out for yourself how much Spectro-Chrome can do for you?

*   *   *   *   *

CHAPTER TWELVE

I BELIEVE

DARIUS DINSHAH, S-C N., (1927-   )

President, Dinshah Health Society

1. I believe wholeheartedly in Spectro-Chrome and I will tell you why. First, the hundreds of satisfied users with whom I have spoken and the innumerable case reports I have read (some were really remarkable) would be enough to convince most anyone. Second, rewording a common advertising phrase, "Spectro-Chrome has been hospital tested, and recommended by doctors", and was not found wanting. Third, my personal experiences including an undiagnosed illness with a 106°F. fever, a shoulder problem which a professional warned me would cause it to "freeze" if I did not follow his instructions (I did not, continuing with Spectro-Chrome instead and it normalated in a few weeks), a persistent and distressing episode of cardiac arrhythmia (normalated with two or three tonations of Orange), and the day-to-day problems seen in raising three active sons. After using Spectro-Chrome at home for a lifetime, frankly, it is difficult to imagine being without it; even the thought is appalling.

2. I believe the Spectro-Chrome System is a completely natural healing method. It does not use dangerous drugs with their attendant side-effects; it does not use blood transfusions with their very real risk of transmitting infections some of which may be fatal; it does not encourage the development of resistant bacteria; it does not use animal-based serums and such. Rather, Spectro-Chrome energizes our inherent reparative processes; and when the powers of construction can no longer maintain a proper balance with those of destruction, it assists in a peaceful death of the physical body.

3. I believe a person's Life Force remains in all their tissues as long as the tissues are viable, so I believe blood transfusions and organ transplants interfere with the spiritual well-being of both the donor and recipient. Further, powerful drugs must be taken continually to prevent transplant rejection; Spectro-Chrome may be contra-indicated in these cases due to the possibility of its overcoming the suppressant drugs' effects and precipitating a foreign-tissue rejection episode. Using the natural with the un-natural may not be an ideal combination.

4. I believe the time *must* come when Spectro-Chrome will be used worldwide. The United States annual expenditure for so-called health care is rapidly approaching one trillion dollars ($1,000,000,000,000) which is over $3000 for every inhabitant. In many countries this is far more than a family earns in a year; for some, health-care of any kind is non-existent so Spectro-Chrome – using the Sun as its Light source – could be a life saver.

5. I believe, as I write this on Christmas day (1st edition, 1984), that no matter what we possess we are poor when we do not have good health. How did Christ demonstrate His power? With money and material wealth? Hardly. He healed the sick, giving them that which could not be bought. I believe, when you have experienced the efficacy of Spectro-Chrome, it would be appropriate to tell someone in need how you were helped. Let each one teach one as some things when shared become larger instead of smaller.

6. I believe the human species was designed to subsist on vegetarian fare; whatever impelled straying from this (famine and/or flood?) does not exist now. It takes about ten pounds of grain fed to animals to produce one pound of meat on the table. The grain wasted in this manner could easily feed all the starving people of the world, and rain-forests would not need to be cleared to grow still more grain. As for the "complete-protein-only-can-be-found-in-meat" myth, it

was dispelled and put to rest long ago; nutritional knowledge has made large strides. Millions of people have lived their entire lives without ever eating a single morsel of flesh (and statistics support the view that they are likely to live longer and more healthfully). I believe the etheric energies of living plants, as seen by Kirlian photography, can be assimilated when eaten and will thereby strengthen us, while animals have more highly developed Life Forces which resist assimilation. Yes, plants are alive but it is specious reasoning to say that we must kill something in order to live so it might as well be animals; I have ears to hear the cries of a dying animal – someday I may be able to hear the plants too but by then I may not need them. I believe, as Dinshah did, that many human ailments are directly or indirectly caused by eating flesh-fowl-fish foods. Investigate, learn, read, visit a slaughter-house, and I fully expect you will come to the same conclusion I have: Blood-foods are not suitable physically, morally, or spiritually, for human consumption. I have heard so many people say, "I couldn't eat meat if I had to kill animals myself", and continue to eat it by ignoring their higher instincts. If we disregard the reality that we are more than just "chemical engines", the price surely must be paid.

7. I believe my father fought the good fight, winning a few legal battles against incredible odds while losing many, but his unbounded faith in his Spectro-Chrome System never wavered. I believe his motto, "Truth may be defeated, but NEVER Conquered" is more than just a motto, it is a certainty. While he did not live to see his dream of "Spectro-Chrome in Every Home" become a reality, there has been a rising level of interest in unorthodox healing methods such as this. I believe Dinshah's goal will come much closer to being attained in my lifetime, and this book is another step to expedite its fulfillment as is the video monolog I taped in 1993 (**My Spectro-Chrome**).

8. I believe life is an ever-changing challenge so one must keep learning or fall behind. Nonetheless, this Chapter is little changed from the lines I wrote in 1984, just up-dated a bit here and there for later editions. If anything, the experiences of yet another decade have amplified my reliance and confidence in Spectro-Chrome, and impelled me to strive more diligently for its advancement.

9. I believe there is a time and place for every healing system ever devised but I am positive I will always place Spectro-Chrome at the top of that list. I believe Spectro-Chrome cannot do everything for everybody; however, it can do so much that it should be the first choice for everyone. I believe such a radical change in medical opinion (barring a major breakthrough) is likely to be far in the future but I see no reason why it cannot start with you.

10. I believe if you carefully follow all the instructions in this volume you too will come to believe that the Power of the Rainbow as embodied in Spectro-Chrome is really God's Gift to all of us.

Truth may be Defeated, but NEVER Conquered

Spectro-Chrome in Every Home

Let There Be Light

CHAPTER THIRTEEN

DuoChrome

1. Yes, **DuoChrome** not Spectro-Chrome. There are similarities but very definite differences between the two techniques. Due to their similarities this method is described here, but because of the distinctive manner of tonation and its effects, the new term DuoChrome is appropriate. This procedure has not had the test of time as Spectro-Chrome has, so greater caution should be exercised if you decide to investigate its effects.

2. Dinshah was well aware from the earliest days that Spectro-Chrome therapy, as we know and use it, is not the last word in the use of Color. In his **Compendium of Spectro-Chrome Therapy** (1922) there is one revealing sentence on page 17, "His present system is based on Single Pole or Predominant Wave operation of the individual Element (Color) but, as soon as a sufficient number has taken up and grounded in this system, he will disclose his more ramified Multipolar System and Process, which will prove a further advancement in this direction...". So, the present Spectro-Chrome system is based on a single predominant frequency in most of its Colors with a later development to be a more complex system with two (or more) frequency crests in each Color. Purple/Magenta/Scarlet are Spectro-Chrome Colors having two peaks in each. Were it not for the interminable harassment he faced, Dinshah surely would have given the healing art an even more powerful technique than Spectro-Chrome is in its present form. We can never know exactly what was in Dinshah's mind but what one person can devise, eventually another will come to similar conclusions. DuoChrome may well have been at least part of his Multipolar technique.

3. The theory behind DuoChrome: Most objects or concepts have two relative aspects or viewpoints: left and right – up and down – hot and cold – yin and yang – good and evil – and so on. In human physiology, from a Spectro-Chrome standpoint, we also find opposites. The more important of these dualities are: brain or intellect (area #1, Green) and reproductive or emotional (area #11, Magenta); spleen (area #6, Violet) and liver (area #7, Red). Areas #1 and #11 represent the ends of the spinal nerves, magnetic meridian; areas #6 and #7, electrical meridian.

4. In order to use the DuoChrome technique, two projectors are required so two Colors can be tonated simultaneously on different areas. The intent here is to balance the top/bottom or left/right areas, and it appears the effect is considerably different from that achieved when tonating Spectro-Chrome Colors at separate tonations.

5. Due to technical differences between the original glass filters (especially, Red/Violet balance) and the presently suggested Roscolene filters, it is strongly recommended that ONLY projectors using Roscolene filters be used for Duo-Chrome tonations.

6. DuoChrome technique is only somewhat different from a typical tonation. For an area #1/#11 DuoChrome tonation, one projector with a Green filter is adjusted so its beam shines across the top of the head (area #1). The second projector, with Magenta filters, is aimed to shine only on area #11.

7. For an area #6/#7 DuoChrome tonation, one projector with a Violet filter is adjusted so its beam shines only on area #6. The second projector, with a Red

filter, is aimed to shine only on area #7. Since these areas are so close to one another, an opaque divider (a sheet of cardboard will do) should be placed vertically between them to prevent the Colors from overlapping. As with all tonations, it is preferable to begin at a Forecast time, head toward the North, etc.

8. The area #1/#11 procedure can be modified, tonating area #1 (always Green) and #22 (any Color) which is considerably more like the original Spectro-Chrome with its Color attributes. Even with relatively limited experience in the area #1/#11 technique, the apparently uncontrolled access to physiologic centers is a compelling reason to strongly recommend DuoChrome tonations of only Green/area #1 and Magenta/area #11. This of course does not apply to usual single Color Spectro-Chrome tonations, DuoChrome #1/#22 or other areas, etc.

9. Another possible balancing set of Colors (TrioChrome): Red on area #7, Green on area #1, and Violet on area #6; these are the three primary Colors and would require three projectors. QuadriChrome could be one step still further, using four projectors to combine the tonations of paragraphs six and seven. Carrying this line of thought to its logical conclusion (MultiChrome) would have projectors with restricted beams, each shining on an area with its appropriate Color, always with Green on #1. The potential applications are almost limitless.

10. DuoChrome tonations of Green/Magenta, areas #1/11, have been tried and found useful but there is not enough data to give a definitive name or attribute as the single Colors have. However, if nothing else, it is an equilibrator with a different character and strength than either Green or Magenta has singly as I have mentioned in the video **My Spectro-Chrome**. For me, it has been effective in correcting a long-standing nasal restriction. For others it may be in a different area; there is also the obvious expectation for its use in emotional or mental conditions. The remainder of the suggestions in these paragraphs are just that: suggestions, which remain to be tested and proven to be of value or otherwise. Whether these techniques were what Dinshah had in mind is immaterial; what does matter is how effective they are. They may establish their worth, at least in some circumstances, but may be too difficult to administer except perhaps in a clinical setting. Obviously, more elaborate equipment is required than for conventional Spectro-Chrome tonations.

11. The intent of this book is to help the reader do all that is safely possible with Spectro-Chrome, DuoChrome, etc. Unfortunately, this Chapter cannot be so specific as we would like. Considering that so many people seem to feel that Light is powerless to cause any physical effect, the strongest reaction I ever experienced with Light was to the point of considerable discomfort. This occurred when experimenting with Colors on area #1/#11 other than the strongly recommended Green/Magenta; there was no lasting effect but it certainly was an eye-opener. The next edition may present more information on this subject if enough interested parties test it, and share their results with us.

12. Spectro-Chrome survived through decades of opposition primarily due to the confidence in it of the "little people". When professionals deserted Dinshah right and left in the 1920s and 30s, lay users/practitioners stood steadfast. We still rely on reports from our members to help maintain Dinshah Health Society as the premier source for information on Color Therapy. Perhaps presumptive, but we are counting on you, too.

CHAPTER FOURTEEN

INEXPENSIVE PROJECTOR PLANS

1. In Chapter three there are several suggestions for Light sources to use with Roscolene filters. All of them have been tried and are usable, with the limitations described. However, a projector made from the plans on the following pages is probably the most practical for Spectro-Chrome tonations. It is inexpensive, consumes little electricity (60-watts), gives a wide beam for systemic tonations, and is easily portable. With a little modification, thin wood such as is used for wall paneling can be substituted for most of the cardboard, making a more durable and attractive though heavier unit. Thin sheet-metal and pop-rivets are another possibility if some simple metal-working tools are at hand, and the ability to use them effectively.

2. Cardboard does not make a projector which looks like a therapeutic device; it has no moving parts and makes no noise. However, the style of the box is totally immaterial. Through the many years he sold them, Dinshah's projectors took numerous different shapes and sizes all with the same basic idea: a Light source and filters (sometimes with a cooling system). So, when you make and use this cardboard projector with the recommended filters, you will be using a projector with the same Color-energy values as those sold by Dinshah, in other words – a genuine **Spectro-Chrome** equipment.

3. This is the material needed:

   About twelve square feet of thin cardboard (about 1/32" thick) such as is found in new shirts to help them hold their shape. Similar material is known in the printing trade as "chipboard" and may be available at commercial printing firms or artist's supply stores.
   Cellophane tape (Scotch tape or similar)
   White glue for paper and cardboard
   Metal-to-paper glue
   A spray-can of flat-black paint.
   A reflector lamp, sometimes called a shop or work lamp; or a swing-arm lamp. Typical lamps look like this:

Shop or work
(reflector) lamp

Swing-arm lamp

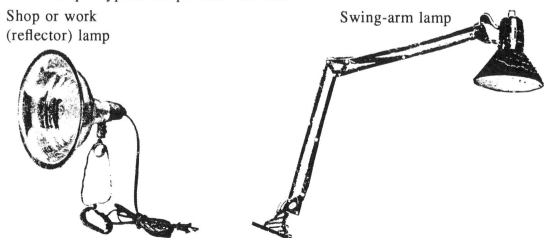

4. If your lamp has a painted interior, Light output can be increased considerably by gluing aluminum foil to the inside of the reflector bowl. Keep the foil an inch or so from the bulb end of the reflector. Do not be concerned if the foil is not perfectly smooth when finished. The following drawings and dimensions were from a prototype projector made with an eight-inch diameter reflector lamp. If your lamp is a different size, you may have to alter the construction details to suit.

5. Cut a piece of cardboard to 3½-inches by 28-inches.

6. Cut one-inch slits one inch apart every three inches along one of the long edges, and bend all the one-inch tabs outward. This makes one-inch square air-vents with a baffle over each like this:

7. Roll the strip into a hoop with the ends overlapping and tabs facing toward the outside. Make the hoop snug around the lamp opening, then fasten the hoop ends together with glue, tape or staples:

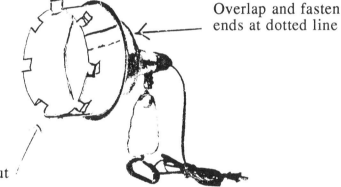

Overlap and fasten
ends at dotted line

One-inch tabs face out

8. Tape and glue (metal-to-paper glue) edge of hoop to lamp opening:

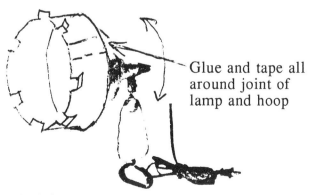

Glue and tape all
around joint of
lamp and hoop

9. Cut a piece of cardboard 10-inches square, and cut a seven-inch hole in its center. Cut four pieces of cardboard five inches by ten inches. Or, if you have a large enough piece of cardboard (20x20 inches) it can be made in one piece:

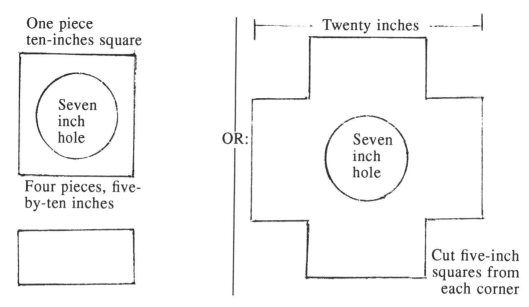

One piece
ten-inches square

Seven inch hole

Four pieces, five-
by-ten inches

OR:

Twenty inches

Seven inch hole

Cut five-inch
squares from
each corner

10. If using five pieces (ten-inches square, and four pieces five by ten inches), tape them together on the dotted lines:

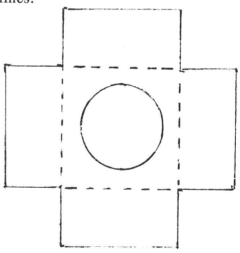

11. Bend up the sides at the dotted lines and tape together at the corners:

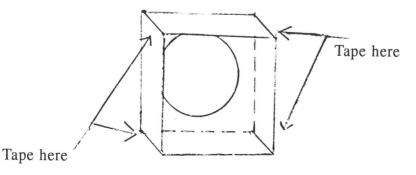

Tape here

Tape here

12. Cut these six pieces of cardboard:
   (a.) Four pieces,   (b.) Two pieces,
   ½-inch by 10-inches   ½-inch by 9-inches

13. Turn the box over so the side with the seven-inch hole (its face) is up. Take the six pieces from paragraph 12 (four of a., and two of b.) and glue them to the face of the box: Glue on here two pieces of a. (½- by 10-inches), one on top of the other

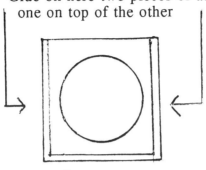

Glue on here two pieces of ½-inch by nine inches, one on top of the other

14. Cut these four pieces of cardboard:
   (c.) One piece   (d.) Three pieces
   ½-inch by eight-inches   One-inch by 10-inches

15. Take the four pieces from paragraph 14 (c. and d.) and glue them to the pieces (a. and b.) already in place:
First, glue a one-by-ten inch piece (d) here   and here

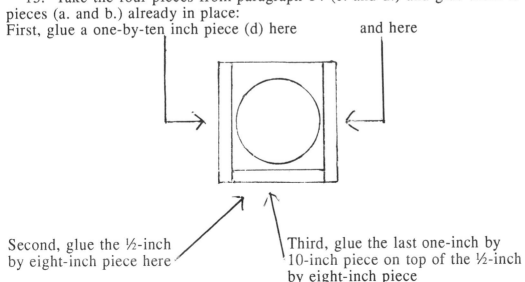

Second, glue the ½-inch by eight-inch piece here

Third, glue the last one-inch by 10-inch piece on top of the ½-inch by eight-inch piece

16. This is an enlarged edge-view of the assembled pieces from paragraphs 12, 13, 14, 15:

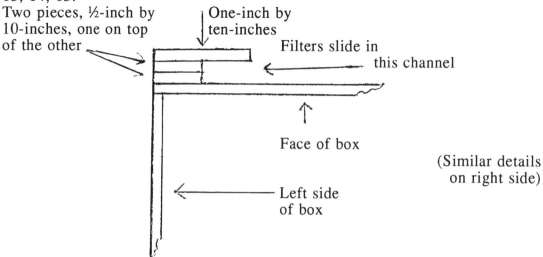

Two pieces, ½-inch by 10-inches, one on top of the other

One-inch by ten-inches

Filters slide in this channel

Face of box

Left side of box

(Similar details on right side)

17. Turn the box face down. Inside the box, on the bottom surface, draw a circle the same size as the hoop:

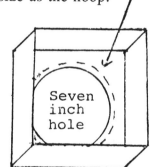

Seven inch hole

If the hoop (now fastened to the lamp) is about eight-inches across, then the drawn circle would be ½-inch from the seven-inch hole

18. Put a good-sized bead of glue on the outer rim of the hoop. Put the glued end of the hoop into the box where the circle is drawn; the circle helps to center the hoop in the box:

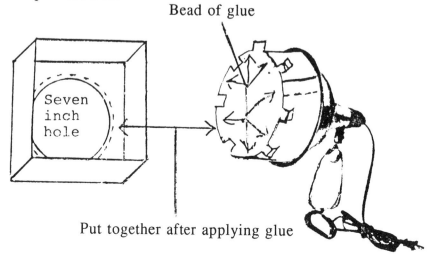

Bead of glue

Seven inch hole

Put together after applying glue

19. Cut 12 cardboard pieces for filter holders, 8¾-inches by 10-inches, and a 7½-inch hole:

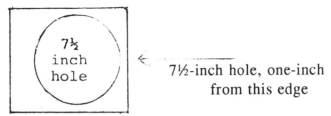

7½
inch
hole

← 7½-inch hole, one-inch
from this edge

20. Assemble the filters for 12 Spectro-Chrome Colors as shown in Chapter three, Color Production. Glue or tape each Color to a filter holder.

21. Place the projector face down. Spray from the back the inside surfaces with flat-black paint to minimize Light reflection. If desired, the outer surfaces may be decorated with wall-paper, paint, vinyl shelf covering, etc.

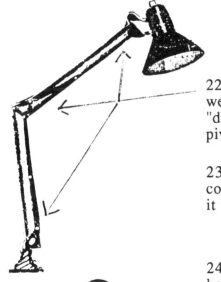

22. If a swing-arm lamp has been used, the extra weight of the projector may cause the lamp to "droop" on its pivots. A little tightening of the pivot bolts should eliminate the problem.

23. Tonate with a 60-watt bulb. Do not be concerned if the plastic filters wrinkle slightly as it will not affect their Color.

24. Reflector lamps should have ventilation holes at the neck. There should be six to eight 3/8-to-½-inch holes. Add or enlarge holes as needed.

25. Even with a 60-watt bulb there is some heat generated by this projector so it is recommended that the projector be kept at least twelve inches from the tonation area.

CHAPTER FIFTEEN

ADDENDUM

1. The Dinshah Health Society publishes an ongoing series of Newsletters, from two to four per year. There may be an announcement (Convention date, etc.), there may be a Color Schedule to add to those in this book, sometimes a comment on medical or scientific developments, or on Spectro-Chrome technique, and so on. The following paragraphs are paraphrased from some of these Newsletters.

2. (11-80). This Society was pivotal in defeating a proposal to fluoridate the water supply of Vineland NJ. While fluorides may delay the formation of dental caries for a time, the long-term harmful effects to humanity (increased number of cases of cancer, Down's syndrome, etc.), and damage to the environment are easily confirmed. In a lawsuit covering 2800 pages of transcript, Pennsylvania Justice John P. Flaherty (now Chief Justice on State Supreme Court) refused to allow water fluoridation in the area then under his jurisdiction, stating, "...the evidence is quite convincing that the addition of sodium fluoride to the public water supply at one part per million is extremely deleterious [emphasis added] to the human body, and a review of the evidence will disclose that there was no convincing evidence to the contrary...". With testimony of such weight leading Justice Flaherty to write such a strong condemnation, do you really think it is wise to drink fluoridated water, especially since the allowable limit is now *four* parts per million? And, why add to your fluoride overload by using fluoridated mouthwash or toothpaste?

3. (4-81). While few and far between, there are some glimmers of Light in our favor. In **Weekly World News** (11-4-80), Faber Birren, a well-known authority on Color for the US Armed Forces, stated, "Colored Light does affect the human body. Anyone who insists otherwise is closing their mind to a great mass of reliable evidence". The article continued on a positive note. Another enlightening essay appeared in **Reader's Digest** (2-81), "How Artificial Light Affects Your Health", page 131 et seq., "...Light is potentially too useful an agency of human health not to be more effectively examined and exploited". These statements of course come as no surprise to Spectro-Chrome users who have been capitalizing on the health benefits of Dinshah's form of Color therapy since 1920.

4. (4-81). American cigarette manufacturers are not required to list the additives used in their products, and there may be as many as 1300 in use, including (from a British list): formic acid, benzoic acid, boric acid, nutmeg, shellac, etc. Tobacco smoke is injurious enough to good health by itself; multiply these effects by those of the additives and smoking must be seen as one of the more pernicious addictions to trap a person.

5. (1-82). Another ray of Light: **The Globe** (12-15-81) carried a front page headline, "Colored Light Cures Arthritis" with the article on page 17 telling of several diseases which had responded to Colored Light or ultra-violet Light. It also gave a table of appropriate Colors to use for several ailments. Further, it listed some of the hazards in using fluorescent lighting.

6. (3-82). Dinshahs are used to taking it on the chin so it is nice to see the other side of the coin occasionally. In 1982, **60 Minutes** (CBS-TV) and **The Phil Donahue Show** (ABC-TV) have spent considerable air time exposing inept medical practitioners and practices, and how little the American Medical Association was doing to police its members. In the **Reader's Digest** (January 1982, page 102 et seq.) "Why Dangerous Doctors Keep Doctoring" is a truly incredible indictment. In one statement it avers that in New York State alone hospital patients may suffer 40,000 injuries annually through medical negligence. On a more positive note, see "The Curative Light" in **Science-82** (April 1982, page 48 et seq); it begins, "Whether from the Sun or from medical lamps, its healing properties are starting to shine."

7. (10-83). **The Merck Manual** is a well-known and respected medical reference volume. As would be expected, it is a highly technical book, but the language on page 1813 (13th edition) is quite plain: "It can be assumed that all exogenous [externally originating] substances given to humans are potentially [their emphasis] carcinogenic, another reason for giving drugs only for a valid indication and only for as long as necessary." No comment needed.

8. (10-83). Whole-blood transfusions are often given in the belief they are essential to preserve life. This long-held view is now being challenged. As long as blood volume is maintained, amazingly little actual blood is necessary. Replacing lost blood with water-based normal-saline solution is more than just satisfactory, it is a superior method according to a Seattle children's hospital (from a report by Dr. Robert Darrow, an American College of Surgeons governor). It also should be noted that a saline-water solution will not cause hepatitis, AIDS, or other blood-transmissible disorders.

9. (10-83). A U.S. Veteran's Administration study found flu vaccinations hamper the liver's ability to remove drugs from the blood-stream. Flu "shots" are often recommended for older persons, and since they are frequently taking other medications, there is a risk of the drugs rising to an overdose level.

10. (10-83). In a controlled study conducted at Portland Optometric Clinic, children with dyslexia or other learning disabilities were treated with lime-green Light (Lemon, chronic alterative by Spectro-Chrome definition) and a deep-red Light (sensory stimulant); the treatments were administered with the patients looking at the Light source. After 16 treatments, their field of vision which previously was considerably narrower than normal (common in patients of this type), was then found to be normal or nearly so. Improvement also was noted in behavior, reading ability, length of attention span, athletic ability, and lessened complaints of headache and eye-strain.

11. (11-83). Homo sapiens is the only creature smart enough to cook his food and dumb enough to eat it. Some of the inevitable loss of nutrients may be minimized by careful cooking practices. For instance, deterioration of chlorophyll in green vegetables can be minimized if the pot is uncovered for the first minutes of cooking to allow volatile acids to escape rather than attack the chlorophyll. Some chefs add baking-soda to the cooking-water to maintain the green color but this destroys vitamin-C and some B-vitamins so it is a practice to be avoided. And, who needs additional dietary sodium?

12. (3-84). An interesting letter was received from an M.D. who also uses Spectro-Chrome. "[Using Roscolene filters] I have observed very good results in

various infectious processes. One remarkable case is a two-year-old child who was severely brain-damaged after drowning in a pool. He has been tonated with motor nervous system schedule #276 [from **Let There Be Light,** Chapter seven] and #266 with Green. Over the last two months there has been constant improvement with decreasing spasticity and seizures, child needs less medications [Valium] and seems to be much more alert."

13. (3-84). We do not know if the US Senate legislated a similar bill, but the US House of Representatives passed HR-12169 on February 7, 1931. It states in section two, "It is further enacted that 'NATUROPATHY', as used in the aforesaid Act, approved February 27, 1929, herewith shall...be composed of the following acts, practices, and usages, - DIAGNOSIS, and PRACTICE of physiological and material sciences of healing as follows, – The physiological and mechanical sciences such as...electrotherapy, phototherapy, chromotherapy [which would include Spectro-Chrome]...". If you know a Naturopath, by all means tell him/her about Spectro-Chrome.

14. (3-84). A liver transplant can cost $200,000 or more, with the continuing expense and hazards of anti-rejection drugs (immunosuppressives). It would be interesting to see what Spectro-Chrome could do for these so-called "incurable" cases before such heroic and expensive measures are taken.

15. (10-84). In one study, two-thirds of the women with fibro-cystic breast disease (nodules) had complete resolution of their problem by stopping intake of tea, coffee, cola drinks, and cocoa, all of which contain methylxanthines (Ohio Medical School, MW/6-79).

16. (10-84). 10 to 15% of serious kidney disease patients may have analgesic nephritis as an underlying cause. Studies have implicated phenacetin and acetaminophen (Tylenol, Datril, etc.). or aspirin and phenacetin taken together, as being capable of producing this type of kidney damage (Philadelphia Bulletin, 11-8-81). No wonder there are so many patients on dialysis.

17. (10-84). A Swiss researcher, Dr. Paul Kouchakoff, reports that a cooked meal (heated above 180-190°F.) causes a rise in white-blood cell count which is a digestive defence reaction. The reaction can be avoided by including raw food in the meal. However, raw food will not help if the cooking temperature exceeded 212°F. such as in canned or pressure-cooked foods. Our assumption is that raw-food enzymes aid digestion to a point where extra defender-cells are not required but cooking above 212°F. further changes food which even the addition of enzymes (raw food) can not ameliorate.

18. (11-85). A study at the University of Florida revealed the danger in treating injuries with common antiseptics such as iodine or hydrogen peroxide. While there is a therapy employing peroxide, when it is used as an antiseptic it may increase the likelihood of an infection developing. Their suggestion is to wash the wound with warm water, dry it and then bandage with dry gauze.

19. (11-85). Prof. Louis Tobian, chief of hypertension research, University of Minnesota Medical School, says his studies indicate that the typical American diet lacks 2/3 of the potassium necessary for sharply reducing the effects of high-blood pressure. What is required daily to give an adequate potassium level (which lowered the death rate in animals an amazing 87%) is: a banana or two, a large potato, some citrus fruit, and some vegetables. As a matter of fact, with

the addition of a little milk and a daily serving of a legume, this is just about the diet recommended by Dinshah decades ago as his **Rational Food of Man**.

20. (10-87). From 1983 to 1986 the only foods (in the US) which were allowed to be preserved with gamma-ray radiation were some spices and seasoning. In 1986, pork and some fruits and vegetables were added to the list. This is the innocent-looking symbol indicating that radiation or "picowaves" have been used on a food:

At present, the words "Treated with radiation" also appear on the package but may not be required after 1988. Cooking destroys enzymes, some vitamins, and the Life Energy, but radiation can cause even greater damage. Radiation can make some bacteria more virulent; it also increases the level of "free radicals" which generate radiolytic products and some of these are potentially carcinogenic. Irradiated grains and nuts are more susceptible to become contaminated with aflatoxin, another cancer causing agent. All considered, it would be prudent to avoid all irradiated food products.

21. (10-87). <u>Candida</u> is a commensal: it is a fungus which lives virtually everywhere and is normally completely harmless. It is opportunistic, causing serious problems when the host's defenses are weakened such as by burns, diabetes, being overweight, systemic drug therapy, organ transplants, hormone birth-control pills, radiation therapy, etc. Candida and certain other fungi can produce an incredible list of disorders, including endocarditis, septicemia, meningitis, osteomyelitis, and also may involve the nails, kidneys, genitals, skin, lungs, etc. Obviously, tonations must be tailored according to the necessities of each case. There are color schedules in this book for several of these conditions, and for those not specifically listed – the Table of Color Attributes can be of service, such as: Lemon ‖**22**‖ as chronic alterative, Turquoise ‖**33**‖ as acute alterative, Magenta ‖**65-67**‖ (or Scarlet ‖**70-74**‖) for the heart and/or kidneys, Orange ‖**6**‖ for the lungs, and so on. Of course, tonations should be begun as instructed in Chapter five, Technique.

22. (2-88). Many prepared-food manufacturers seem to be climbing on the dietary fiber band-wagon. One nutritional supplement supplier brags, "Six times the fiber content of a wheat-bran tablet!" The idea seems to be: Continue with your junk-food diet, and our tablet will take care of all your needs. What foolishness!! Your body needs vitamins, minerals, enzymes, together with fiber rather than a chunk of indigestible matter taken as a pill. Consuming foods in as near to their natural state as possible (in an adequate vegetarian diet) makes additional fiber unnecessary and undesirable.

23. (10-88). Boron has not been generally recognized as an essential element in human nutrition, but this may be a dangerous assumption. **Health Confidential** (5-88) reports that boron reduces our excretion of minerals necessary to keep our bones strong (calcium/magnesium/phosphorus), and this process lessens the likelihood of developing osteoporosis. Boron is found in leafy vegetables,

legumes, nuts and some fruit. In most circumstances, careful vegetarians should have a plentiful supply of all trace elements, vitamins and minerals whether they are recognized as essential or not.

24. (11-90). We have always believed prevention is better than cure. A recent study of 41 patients claimed heart disease can be, in some cases, reversed without drugs or surgery by controlling stress, clean living (whatever that means) and a low-fat <u>vegetarian</u> diet. The researchers say more studies are needed to answer important questions. Why? A low-fat vegetarian diet MUST be good for you, why wait for yet another study? (AP D.J. 7/21/90)

25. (10-91). For many centuries earrings have been worn as adornments. A new fad is "body-piercing" where rings, pins or other objects are anchored into the skin, tongue, or almost anywhere else. Something to ponder: what happens when any of these objects passes through an acupuncture point or an obscure energy convergence site? Testing with biokinesis should show that these practices are not in anyone's best interest.

26. (2-90). After so many years, few people now realize the problems and harassment Dinshah faced in his battle for Spectro-Chrome. Reproduced here is a flier he printed circa 1955. While nothing like what is shown has happened since then, it documents the "legal" power which can be brought to bear against those who dare raise opposition to entrenched medical interests.

PRESENT DAY JUSTICE IN AMERICA!!

A private home, under the glorious Constitution of the United States of America, is considered the "castle" of the owner; yet, between the years 1945 and 1948, hundreds of American homes were entered by Deputy United States Marshals and the Color Projectors For Healing belonging to satisfied purchasers were pulled out and destroyed, without compensation to the owners.

IT WAS DONE TO DOWN DINSHAH,

the Originator of his novel, proven, unique Science of Healing!

HE IS STILL THERE!!

Truth May be defeated — but Never conquered!!!

27. (12-91). Dinshah firmly insisted that no electrical device (other than the projector) be near a person being tonated. A recent **Popular Science** magazine article spelled out how we are continually immersed in electro-magnetic fields

(EMFs) from the devices, wiring, etc. in our homes and workplaces, and how we may be affected. An **Associated Press** article focussed on the increased possibility of developing leukemia, with the highest figure (2.8 times) for those who often used an electric hair dryer. This may be because the typical dryer draws a very large current, is used close to the brain, and its heating element is usually in a circular form which may direct its force like a solenoid. Electric blankets were indicted similarly many years ago and should be avoided.

28. (12-92). We had several different Spectro-Chrome projectors on display at our 1992 Convention. It gave us an opportunity to use a photometer (Light-measuring instrument), comparing the Light output of a 1500-watt Graduate model Spectro-Chrome projector to that of the inexpensive 60-watt projector made from the plans in Chapter 14. At a distance of about three feet, a typical tonation distance, their Light was to all intents and purposes <u>identical</u> because the Graduate model has an 18"-long lens system while the 60-watter has no lens and a large filter opening. This confirms our long-held contention that a Spectro-Chrome projector can do just as well with a small bulb. Further, the first patient Dinshah treated with Color therapy (1897, in India) was with the illumination from a kerosene lantern which may have been less than that of a 10-watt bulb.

29. (12-92). We cannot emphasize our feelings too strongly regarding so-called "full-spectrum" bulbs which, according to the advertising of **Chromalux**, by using Neodymium are "able to absorb yellow and other dulling components of the spectrum – as a result the light is purified". Incredible nonsense!! Remove Yellow frequencies from the spectrum and it is then "purified"? Every part of the complete spectrum is essential for the well-being of one part or another of the human constitution; remove a Color and the organs normally energized by that frequency will suffer. The Table of Color Attributes in six will show the organs and systems which may be affected eventually from this folly. The only benefit from these Neodymium bulbs is to the sellers: About $10 each compared to regular incandescent bulbs (about 59 cents) which are far from perfect but they DO have ALL visible Color frequencies.

30. (6-94). Dinshah, born in India where the importance of proper breathing (prana) has been recognized for centuries, incorporated this knowledge in Spectro-Chrome in the form of the heart/breathing rate ratio and the Variant Breath Forecast (known in earlier years as the Favorscope). A recent article touted the use of a short, crutch-like device, **hamsadanda**, for controlling how each nostril breathes by pressing on armpit nerves. The Spectro-Chrome system teaches and utilizes the forward/backward cycle of the nostrils' pressure. Tinkering with this important function must not be taken lightly or on a whim, and must be emphatically discouraged. Each nostril is designed to have a certain pressure at a given time of the day or night, advancing and receding on a two hour and fifty-six minute cycle. Their rhythmic activity is a mirror of the Sympathetic Nervous System activity within. Trying to maintain the nostrils at an even or other artificial level is to invite health problems. Those who advocate this unnatural practice may be unaware of the harm it can cause.

31. (6-94). **Semolina, made from 100% durum wheat** are words seen on almost all packages of spaghetti, macaroni and other pastas, but what does "Made from 100%..." really mean? A phone call to a large, well known flour-mill in Texas gave us this authoritative answer: Semolina is the same as any other type

of WHITE FLOUR. The base ingredient is entirely (100%) of a certain variety of wheat (durum) but processing removes the bran and germ–presto-chango–the 100% durum becomes white flour. The statement of 100% etc. can be factually correct but so very easily misunderstood; perhaps that is the intent. There is real WHOLE-WHEAT pasta available; look at the ingredient list which must specifically say "whole wheat" rather than "Made from...".

32. (10-94). Several recent segmented news programs have had considerable coverage on problems with E.Coli-0157H7 in the US slaughterhouse industry. TURNING POINT (ABC-TV 10-12-94) stated that there were thousands of illnesses and hundreds of deaths annually attributable to foods contaminated with that bacteria. The commentator said something like, "Outside of becoming a vegetarian, we will have to learn how to deal with this." So where is the problem? From an economic, moral, health, environmental standpoint, the simple answer is to be a vegetarian. Unfortunately, for all too many this is much easier said than done; for me it has not been difficult as I was born to a vegetarian family and have continued and fully expect to end as one. For those not so fortunate, the vegetarian movement has gained much strength and even popularity in the last ten to twenty years. There are now many vegetarian groups/cookbooks/etc. to help those who make the intelligent decision to change.

33. (10-94). Most physicians now in practice have never known a time without the availability of antibiotics. Through decades of use and abuse of these drugs, the "tougher" germs have survived so there is a growing list of disorders which often do not respond to this type of therapy–they have developed *RESISTANCE*. It takes an incredibly long time and large amount of money to find, test, and market a new and effective antibiotic, and a drug may be useful only against a particular germ. All of these agents work by "poisoning" a susceptible germ rather than energizing the patient's body to do what it has been designed to do: fight its own battles. Spectro-Chrome has a fair-sized arsenal for that purpose– Green/Turquoise/Blue/Indigo/Violet, and Yellow in some circumstances. If those "invaders" somehow ever develop resistance to Spectro-Chrome (an unlikely event) then humanity will really have a problem.

34. (10-94) A survey of very old people found these four personal traits to be the most important for achieving a ripe old age:

a. The ability to cope with any type of loss: Relatives, monetary, business, etc.

b. Involvement: Helping others rather than a preoccupation with our own financial, health, or other problems.

c. Activity: Housework, formal exercise, gardening, anything to keep the blood circulation and lymphatic system moving.

d. Optimism: A cheerful mental state, look on the bright side, bread doesn't always fall on the buttered side.

The one important item missing from that list is a healthful diet but there may not have been an inquiry about it on their questionnaire.

*   *   *   *   *

As Commander, NY Police Reserve Air Service, 1918.   By order of Special Deputy Police
Commissioner Rodman Wanamaker, Dinshah organized a complete Air Force to protect the
City of New York. For his services, he was presented with the Liberty Medal by the Mayor.

Part of a typical classroom arrangement for physics
demonstrations pertaining to Spectro-Chrome (circa 1925)

Dinshah with part of his Staff—New York Police Reserve Air Service

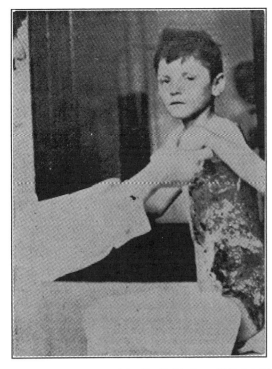
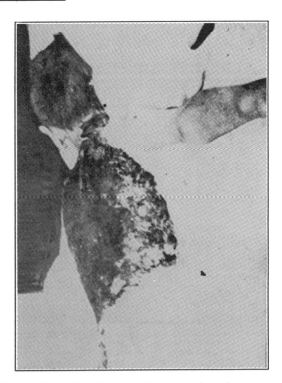

Grace Shirlow, tonated by Dr. Baldwin at Philadelphia Woman's Hospital. Upper photos were taken about two weeks after admission. Lower photos, about eighteen months later. See Chapter Eleven for particulars regarding this outstanding example of healing with the Spectro-Chrome System.

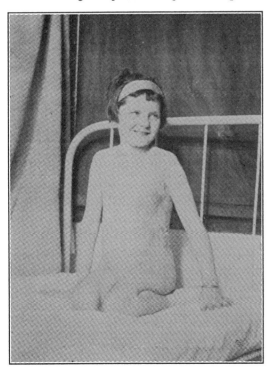
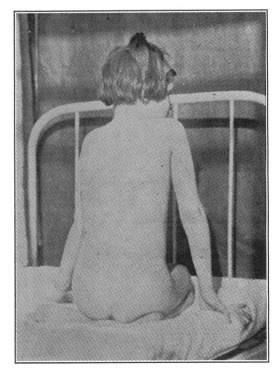

LET THERE BE LIGHT

Type set, copyrighted, and published by:
Dinshah Health Society, P O Box 707, Malaga NJ 08328 USA
December 1997

Fourth edition
ISBN 0-933917-17-1

Printed and bound in the United States of America.

Bibliography:
The Spectro-Chrome System, 2nd edition (1979), Darius Dinshah
Let There Be Light, 3rd edition (1996), Darius Dinshah
The Merck Manual, 16th edition (1992); Dr Robert Berkow, editor.

* * * * *

Cuneiform symbols used by ancient Persians (page four):

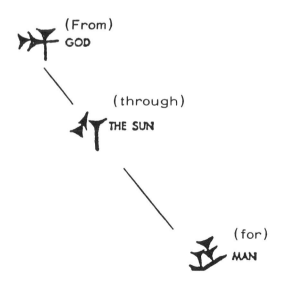

EDUCATIONAL MATERIAL AVAILABLE FROM
DINSHAH HEALTH SOCIETY
P.O. BOX 707, MALAGA NJ 08328 USA

A. **Let There Be Light,** Darius Dinshah. 12 concise Chapters cover most theoretical and practical aspects of Spectro-Chrome therapy. Includes: Color production, Light sources, filter supplier, Spectro-Chrome definitions, 78 Color attributes, 327 Color schedules for 400 diagnosed and obvious health conditions, 600 indexed medical and common names, 3-years' hospital use documentation, use on animals, Color/element/sound equivalents, etc. It is written in easy-to-understand language and terms for layperson or practitioner. Items **B, C, D, H,** listed below are included in the text, and important details from item **J.** Second edition, 164 pages, hardbound.

B. **Dr. Baldwin Testifies.** An excerpt from a book, <u>Triumph of Spectro-Chrome</u>, which detailed the genesis and testimony of a lawsuit fought and won by the originator of Spectro-Chrome therapy, Dinshah P. Ghadiali. Six physicians and lay practitioners testified in his behalf. This excerpt is the sworn testimony of Dr. Kate W. Baldwin as she recounted some of her experiences with Spectro-Chrome in her private practice and in the Philadelphia PA Woman's Hospital where she was its Senior Surgeon for 23 years. (This is included in Chapter 11 of Let There Be Light, item **A**). 26 page booklet.

C. **Therapeutic Value of Light and Color,** Dr. Kate W. Baldwin. Abstract of a paper presented at a meeting of the Medical Society of Pennsylvania, held at the Philadelphia Medico-Chirurgical Hospital. From the Atlantic Medical Society Journal, April 1927. (This is in the Preface of item **A.**) Leaflet.

D. **Philadelphia Woman's Hospital Trustees' Minutes,** excerpt. Documentation/commentary on Dr. Kate W. Baldwin's using Spectro-Chrome at this hospital. The Minutes are photographically reproduced from the original volume, with added side-notes and references. (This is included in Chapter 11 of Let There Be Light, item **A**) Leaflet.

E. **Donations.** As an IRS recognized non-profit organization (501, C-3), donations to this Society are tax deductible under present regulations, with certain restrictions on the amount.

F. **Calendar year membership.** Includes Variant Breath Forecast for your local area, and Newsletters when published (usually three or four per year). Please complete the membership application at the end of this book or copy the information requested.

G. **Itisometer Manual.** The Itisometer was a sensitive electric thermometer used to measure the activity of internal organs by sensing the temperature over them. 44 Itisometers were hand-made, the last in 1942. This is a reproduction of the Manual on technique, with updated material for using a presently available $650 substitute electronic unit. The technique is quite involved, partly due to the necessity of using additional charts to translate temperature readings to tonation Colors. Booklet, with five enlarged charts.

H. The Inexpensive Projector, plans. Easy-to-follow step-by-step instructions to make a Color projector with common materials (40- or 60-watt reflector lamp/ cardboard/glue, about $10 plus filters). About two to three hours to cut and assemble. (This is Chapter 14 of item **A**.) Eight pages, 20 illustrations.

I. Es werde Licht (Praktischer Leitfaden fur Dinshahs 12-Farben Chromopathie). German 1989 edition of item **A** above (Let There Be Light). Its additional pages are mostly due to the complexity of the German language. 192 pages, hardbound.

J. History of Spectro-Chrome. Dinshah P. Ghadiali edited the Spectro-Chrome and Visible Spectrum Researcher magazines, from 1922 to 1957 (240 issues). Their 6000+ pages cover thousands of case reports from abscesses to x-ray burns; Dinshah's editorial comments; transcripts of several lawsuits; hundreds of articles by professionals who used Spectro-Chrome exclusively or with other methods; technical details as they were introduced: Favorscope (Forecast), Sympathometer, Itisometer, etc.; offers by Dinshah to donate his work and Institute to the AMA, or US government; and much more.
6000+ pages, seven clothbound volumes.

K. Therapeutische wert von Licht und Farbe. German language version of item **C** above. Large leaflet.

L. Der Preiswerte Farblicht Projektor. German language version of item **H** above. Eight pages, 20 illustrations.

M. Spectro-Chrome Metry Encyclopedia, Dinshah P. Ghadiali. 117 Chapters thoroughly cover the development and theory of Spectro-Chrome. Written in 1933, the first two editions spanned 1200 pages in three volumes. Their wide margins and numerous pages pertaining to courses taught by Dinshah have been deleted, but the text has not been edited. While some scientific views conflict with some of Dinshah's, it remains for history and you the reader to judge. (Let There Be Light, item **A** above, is recommended for those new to Spectro-Chrome. Though based on Dinshah's teachings, item **A** has much greater emphasis on the practical application of Spectro-Chrome.)
3rd edition, 240 pages; 169 charts, tables, illustrations; hardbound.

N. My Spectro-Chrome, Darius Dinshah. Video monolog version of item **A** above (LTBL), with much additional material: how to calculate the Forecast; how the original glass filters were matched (attuned); spectroscopic demonstration showing why fluorescent and neodymium lamps can eventually cause problems; views of old projectors/Itisometer/Institute, etc. Recommend following along with a copy of **LTBL** (item **A**), Chapter by Chapter. USA, VHS NTSC format; run time: 5 hours/54 minutes.

O. My Spectro-Chrome, Darius Dinshah. Video, PAL/European format – two cassette set (same content as item **N**).

P. Spectro-Chrome Magazines, abridged. The complete set (item **J, History**, above) is very long, and in some respects repetitious. This version consists of 41 selected and edited Spectro-Chrome magazines with emphasis on earlier years. Many articles by professionals. 496 pages, softbound, single volume.

Q. Spectro-Chrome Guide, Darius Dinshah. Condensed version of **Let There Be Light** (item **A**, above). For readers who want to learn basic Spectro-Chrome technique; emphasis is on "how-to" with very little "why-is-so". Ten Chapters, 104 pages, hardbound.

A non-profit, scientific, educational,
membership corporation

609 692-4686

DINSHAH HEALTH SOCIETY
P O Box 707
Malaga NJ 08328 USA

Please enroll me as a member so I may learn and help others to learn some of the
lesser known methods of restoring and maintaining health.

☐ I am a new member.   ☐ I am/have been a member.

(Mr, Mrs, Rev,
Ms, Miss, Dr.)_____ _____ Gender_____

Address_____ Apt #_____

City,
State, Zip_____ Phone #_____

I learned of this
Occupation_____ Society from _____

My local   For foreign   From large
time zone_____ Countries: I live____km City_____
                            (North, East, South, West)

Comments_____

_____

_____

Date_____ Signed _____

* * * * *

Membership to end of year (or following year if after Sept. 30th) $3 as of 1997.
Includes Variant Breath Forecast for your area; and Newsletters as published.

A non-profit, scientific, educational,
membership corporation

609 692-4686

DINSHAH HEALTH SOCIETY
P O Box 707
Malaga NJ 08328 USA

Please enroll me as a member so I may learn and help others to learn some of the lesser known methods of restoring and maintaining health.

☐ I am a new member.   ☐ I am/have been a member.

(Mr, Mrs, Rev,
Ms, Miss, Dr.)_____ _____ Gender_____

Address_____ Apt #_____
City,
State, Zip_____ Phone #_____

Occupation_____ Society from _____
I learned of this

My local   For foreign   From large
time zone_____ Countries: I live____km City_____
                         (North, East, South, West)

Comments_____

_____

_____

Date_____ Signed _____

* * * * *

Membership to end of year (or following year if after Sept. 30th) $3 as of 1997. Includes Variant Breath Forecast for your area; and Newsletters as published.

A non-profit, scientific, educational,
membership corporation

609 692-4686

DINSHAH HEALTH SOCIETY
P O Box 707
Malaga NJ 08328 USA

Please enroll me as a member so I may learn and help others to learn some of the
lesser known methods of restoring and maintaining health.
    ☐ I am a new member.   ☐ I am/have been a member.

(Mr, Mrs, Rev,
Ms, Miss, Dr.)_____ _____ Gender_____

Address_____ Apt #_____
City,
State, Zip_____ Phone #_____
                                     I learned of this
Occupation_____ Society from _____
My local   For foreign   From large
time zone_____ Countries: I live____km City_____
                            (North, East, South, West)

Comments_____

_____

_____

Date_____ Signed _____

                    *   *   *   *   *

Membership to end of year (or following year if after Sept. 30th) $3 as of 1997.
Includes Variant Breath Forecast for your area; and Newsletters as published.